NUCLEUS

ENGLISH FOR SCIENCE AND TECHNOLOGY
GENERAL SCIENCE

New Edition with Reading Texts

Lonnie Kahn & Co. Ltd.,
5 Nachlath Benjamin Street,
PO Box 4489,
TEL. AVIV.

Contents

		page
Unit 1	Properties and Shapes	1
Unit 2	Location	12
Unit 3	Structure	20
Unit A	Revision	29
Unit 4	Measurement 1	31
Unit 5	Process 1 Function and Ability	40
Unit 6	Process 2 Actions in Sequence	49
Unit B	Revision	60
Unit 7	Measurement 2 Quantity	63
Unit 8	Process 3 Cause and Effect	74
Unit 9	Measurement 3 Proportion	86
Unit C	Revision	95
Unit 10	Measurement 4 Frequency, Tendency, Probability	98
Unit 11	Process 4 Method	108
Unit 12	Consolidation	118
Glossary		128

Unit 1   Properties and Shapes

Section 1   One-dimensional and two-dimensional shapes

1. Look at these:

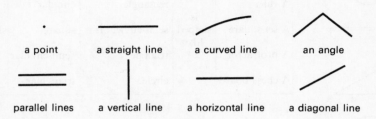

a point   a straight line   a curved line   an angle

parallel lines   a vertical line   a horizontal line   a diagonal line

Now read this and answer the questions:

> The letter 'E' has one vertical line and three horizontal lines. It also has four angles.
> Which of these letters are described below?
> D, M, C, H, F, L, Z, B.

a) A letter with 2 horizontal lines and 1 vertical line.
b) A letter with 1 curved line and no straight lines.
c) A letter with 2 curved lines and 1 vertical line.
d) A letter with 2 parallel vertical lines, 1 horizontal line and 4 angles.
e) A letter with 2 vertical lines and 2 diagonal lines.

Now write sentences describing these signs:

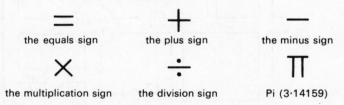

the equals sign   the plus sign   the minus sign

the multiplication sign   the division sign   Pi (3·14159)

2. Look at these figures and answer the questions:

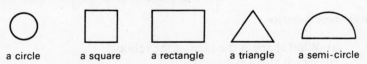

a circle   a square   a rectangle   a triangle   a semi-circle

a) Which figure is curved?
b) Which figures have parallel sides?
c) Which figure always has equal sides?

1

d) Which figure may have equal sides?
e) Which figure has 3 angles?
f) Which figure has a curved side and a straight side?

Now make sentences from the table:

Example : A coin is shaped like a circle. It is circular in shape.

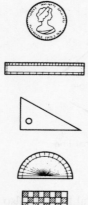

A coin			square.		rectangular	
A ruler			rectangle.		circular	
A set square	is shaped like a		semi-circle.	It is	square	in shape.
A protractor			triangle.		semi-circular	
A chess-board			circle.		triangular	

3. Look at this plan of a town:

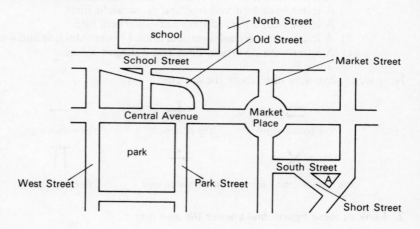

Answer these questions:

a) What shape is the plan of the school?
b) Which street is curved?
c) What shape is area A?
d) Which area is square?
e) Name two streets which are parallel.

2

f) Are Old Street and School Street parallel?
g) Which part is roughly circular in shape?
h) Which streets meet at an angle of 90 degrees (at right angles)?
i) Which streets meet at a different angle?

Section 2   Three-dimensional shapes

4. Look and answer:

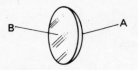

This is a lens. One *surface* is *curved* and the other is *flat*. Which is which?

Look at these solids:

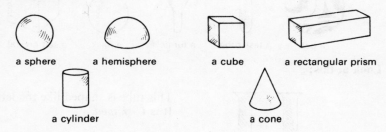

a sphere   a hemisphere   a cube   a rectangular prism

a cylinder   a cone

Now describe them:

Example: A cube has 6 surfaces. They are all flat and square.

5. Look and read:

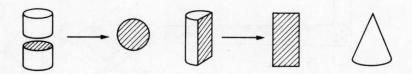

The *cross-section* of a cylinder is circular. The *longitudinal* section is rectangular. The sides of a cylinder are parallel. The sides of a cone are *tapering*.

Answer these questions:

a) What shape is the cross-section of a sphere?
b) What shape is the longitudinal section of a hemisphere?
c) What shape is the cross-section of a cube?
d) Which solid is rectangular in cross-section?
e) In longitudinal section, are the sides of a cylinder parallel or tapering?

3

f) In longitudinal section, are the sides of a cone parallel or tapering?

g) What shape is the cross-section of a cone?

6. Complete these:

Cylindrical = shaped like a _____
Cubic = shaped like a _____
Conical = shaped like a _____
Spherical = shaped like a _____

Now describe the shapes of these objects:

Example: A ball is spherical in shape.

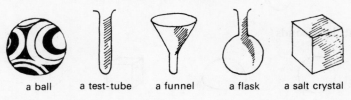

a ball   a test-tube   a funnel   a flask   a salt crystal

7. Look at this:

This tube is shaped like the letter 'U'.
It is *U-shaped*.

Describe the shapes of the following:

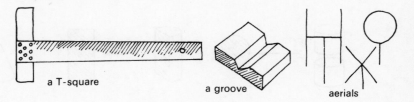

a T-square   a groove   aerials

These objects are used to describe shapes:

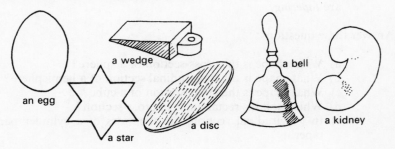

an egg   a wedge   a star   a disc   a bell   a kidney

4

Now describe the following objects:

Example: A potato is egg-shaped.

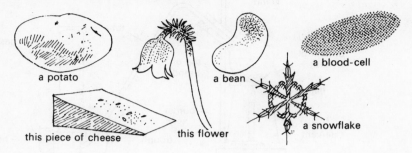

a potato

a bean

a blood-cell

this piece of cheese

this flower

a snowflake

8. Look at this picture:

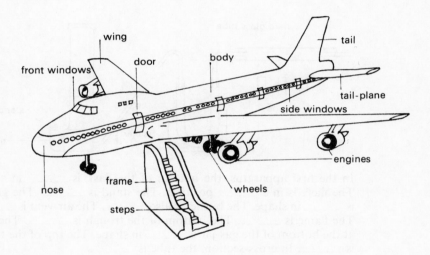

wing

tail

door

body

front windows

tail-plane

side windows

engines

nose

frame

wheels

steps

Now say whether these statements are true or false. Correct the false statements.

   a) The tail is nearly triangular in shape.
   b) The door is flat.
   c) The steps are parallel to each other.
   d) The sides of the frame are curved.
   e) The tail-plane is wing-shaped.
   f) All the windows are circular.
   g) The engines are nearly cylindrical.
   h) The wheels are cubic in shape.
   i) The front of the plane is cylindrical.
   j) The nose is tapering.
   k) The wings are at right angles to the body.

9. Look at these diagrams and complete the descriptions:

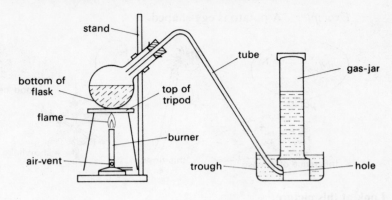

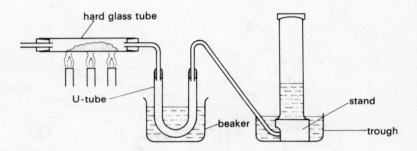

In the first apparatus, the bottom of the flask is _____ in shape. The flask is in a _____ position. The stand is _____. The gas-jar is _____ in shape. The burner is also _____. The air-vent is _____. The flame is _____. The bottom of the trough is _____. The hole at the bottom of the gas-jar is _____ in shape. The top of the tripod is _____. In cross-section, the tube is _____.

Now make as many sentences as you can describing the second apparatus.

Section 3   Properties of materials

10. Look and read:

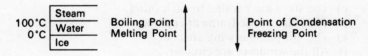

Ice is *solid*. Water is *liquid*. Steam is *gaseous*. Steam and water are *fluids*.

	Oxygen	
−183 °C	Oxygen	Boiling Point
−218·4 °C	Oxygen	Melting Point

	Neon	
−245·9 °C	Neon	Boiling Point
−248·7 °C	Neon	Melting Point

Complete these statements:

a) At −183°C oxygen changes from the gaseous state to the _____ state.

b) At −218·4°C oxygen changes from the liquid state to . . . .

c) At 183°C oxygen is in the _____ state.

d) At −246°C neon is in the _____ state.

e) At −220°C oxygen is in the _____ state.

f) Steam, water, ice, oxygen, neon: all these are fluids except _____.

11. Read the following properties of materials and complete the examples:

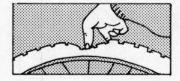

A *brittle* material *breaks* easily; eg glass, . . .

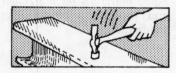

A *tough* material does not break easily; eg steel, . . .

A *hard* material is difficult to *scratch*; eg glass, . . .

A *soft* material is easy to scratch; eg chalk, . . .

A *flexible* material *bends* easily; eg rubber, . . .

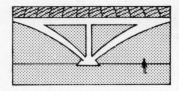

A *rigid* material does not bend easily; eg concrete, . . .

Answer these questions:

   a) Why does a glass beaker break if you drop it?
   b) Why doesn't a polythene beaker break?
   c) Why is butter easy to cut?
   d) Why can a diamond cut glass?
   e) Why do the branches of a tree bend in the wind?
   f) Why don't the walls of a house bend in the wind?
   g) Which is more flexible: a wooden ruler or a plastic ruler?
   h) What are the different properties of green wood (on a tree) and dry wood?

12. Read and complete these:

Some materials have a *smooth* surface; they produce little *friction* when they are rubbed; eg ice, . . .

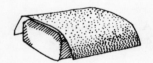

Some materials have a *rough* surface and produce a lot of friction; eg sandpaper, . . .

Materials which are *soluble* in water *dissolve* easily; eg salt, . . .

Materials which are *insoluble* do not dissolve; eg glass, . . .

You can see through *transparent* materials; eg water, . . .

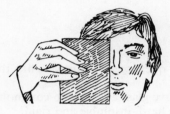

You cannot see through *translucent* materials but the light passes through them; eg dirty water, . . .

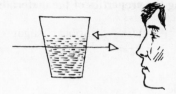

You cannot see through *opaque* materials and the light cannot pass through them; eg metal, . . .

Combustible materials *burn* easily; eg wood, . . .

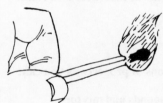

Non-combustible materials do not burn, eg stone, . . .

Read this and choose the right properties:

A material which is used for making clothes must be solid/fluid, brittle/tough, soft/hard, rigid/flexible, smooth/rough, opaque/transparent and soluble/insoluble.

Complete these sentences:

One material with these properties is wool. Others are _____ and _____.

Steel is not generally used for clothes because it is . . . .
Glass is unsuitable because it is _____, _____ and _____.

Now suggest different properties which are suitable for the following purposes and give examples of materials with the right properties:

    a) For the body of a car we need a material which is _____, _____, _____ and _____, eg _____.
    b) For a window . . . , eg _____.
    c) For a cooking pot . . . , eg _____.

13. Complete the following table, giving the properties of the materials:

	steel	glass	rubber	sugar	wood
tough/brittle	tough				
soft/hard	hard				
soluble/insoluble	insoluble				
combustible/non-combustible	non com-bustible				
flexible/rigid	rigid				
transparent/opaque	opaque				

Look at these examples and make other questions and answers like them:

    Example: What properties have glass and steel in common?
                Glass and steel are hard, insoluble and rigid.

Section 4   Reading

14. Read this text. Find as many descriptions of property as you can:

The properties of elements, compounds and mixtures
A substance may be an element, a compound or a mixture. An element, such as nitrogen or iron, cannot be broken down into simpler substances. When two or more elements combine, they form a compound.
5   When elements combine to form compounds, there is a chemical reaction. Some properties of the elements change during the chemical reaction. For example, the element chlorine (Cl) is a poisonous yellow gas. Sodium (Na), on the other hand, is a soft silvery-white metal which reacts violently with water. However, if these elements
10 combine, they form sodium chloride, or salt. This is a harmless white substance.
    When substances are mixed without a chemical reaction, they do not change their properties. Thus a mixture of sand and salt is yellowish-white in colour. It tastes both salty and gritty. If we put the
15 mixture in water, the salt will dissolve, because it is soluble. But the sand will not dissolve.
    Every substance has a melting point and a boiling point. The former is the temperature at which it changes from solid to liquid. The latter is the temperature at which it changes from liquid to gas. These
20 changes are called changes of state. Sometimes the properties of a

substance change when it changes its state. For example, if the temperature of oxygen falls below $-183°C$, it changes from a colourless gas to a bluish liquid, which is highly magnetic.

Now answer these questions:

a) List the descriptions of property which you have found. What do they describe in the passage? Use them to describe other substances.

Example: Colourless. In the passage, it says that oxygen is a colourless gas. Water is also colourless. It is a colourless liquid.

b) What is the difference between an element and a compound? Give some examples of each.
c) What is the difference between a compound and a mixture? Say two things about compounds which are not true about mixtures.
d) Sodium chloride is harmless. Are sodium and chlorine harmless? Give reasons for your answer.
e) Why does salt dissolve in water and why does sand not dissolve?
f) What is the boiling point of oxygen?

Unit 2   Location

Section 1   Positions on two dimensions

1. Look and read:

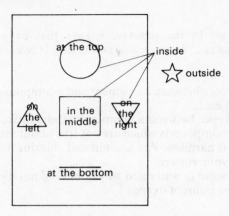

The words give the positions of the shapes *in relation to the rectangle*.

Make questions and answers like the following:

> *Example:*   What is there *at the top of* the rectangle?
> There is a circle at the top of the rectangle.

2. Now look at this:

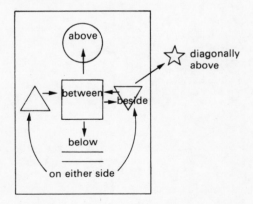

The words give the positions of the shapes *in relation to one another*.

Make questions and answers like the following:

> *Example:*   Where is the circle?
> The circle is above the square.

3. Look and read:

Sc	Ti	V	Cr	Mn	Fe	Co	Ni	Cu	Zn
Scandium	Titanium	Vanadium	Chromium	Manganese	Iron	Cobalt	Nickel	Copper	Zinc
Y	Zr	Nb	Mo	Tc	Ru	Rh	Pd	Ag	Cd
Yttrium	Zirconium	Niobium	Molybdenum	Technetium	Ruthenium	Rhodium	Palladium	Silver	Cadmium
La	Hf	Ta	W	Re	Os	Ir	Pt	Au	Hg
Lanthanum	Hafnium	Tantalum	Tungsten	Rhenium	Osmium	Iridium	Platinum	Gold	Mercury

Above there is a table of some elements. The elements are arranged in horizontal *rows* and vertical *columns*.

Give the positions of the following elements in relation to the whole table:

> *Examples:* Lanthanum is at the bottom, on the left.
> Vanadium is *in the third column from the left*, at the top.
> Cobalt is *in the top row, near* the middle.

Tungsten, cadmium, zinc, gold, scandium, iron.

Now give the position of these elements in relation to others:

> *Example:* Osmium is beside and *to* the right of rhenium.

Cobalt in relation to nickel and iron
Niobium in relation to molybdenum
Platinum and mercury in relation to gold
Gold in relation to silver
Iron in relation to rhodium
Silver in relation to zinc
Silver in relation to gold

4. Read these sentences which give other positions:

Cobalt is *next to*, or *adjacent to*, nickel.
Iron is not adjacent to nickel because cobalt is between them.
Manganese is *in line with* copper and gold is in line with hafnium.
Yttrium is *near* tantalum but *far from* zinc.

Now say whether these statements are true or false. Correct the false statements.

a) Silver is diagonally above nickel.
b) Zinc is in line with scandium.
c) Molybdenum and ruthenium are on either side of technetium.
d) Gold is adjacent to mercury.
e) Iron is beside and to the right of cobalt.
f) Gold is vertically below silver.

13

g) Vanadium is near cadmium.

h) Mercury is at the bottom of the table, on the right.

i) Copper is between nickel and zinc.

j) Manganese is in the middle row.

k) Silver is in the third column from the right.

Section 2   Positions on three dimensions

5. Look and read:

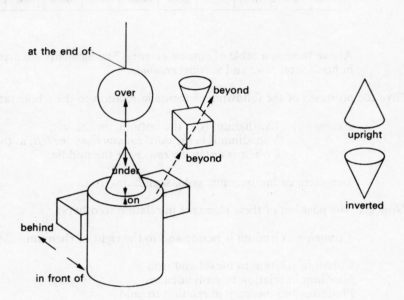

Note: The sphere is *above* all the other solids, but it is *over* only the cone and the middle of the cylinder.

Now make questions and answers:

Example: Where is the sphere in relation to the upright cone?
The sphere is *over* the upright cone.

sphere . . . upright cone.   upright cone . . . cylinder.
upright cone . . . sphere.   cylinder . . . upright cone.
rectangular solid . . . cylinder.   inverted cone . . . cube.
cylinder . . . rectangular solid.   cube . . . inverted cone.
cube . . . rectangular solid.   sphere . . . line.

14

6. Look and read:

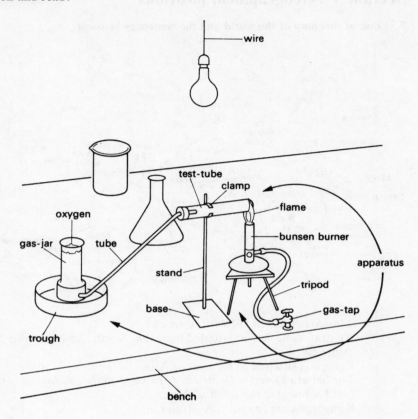

Now complete this description:

a) There is a gas-jar . . . of the apparatus.
b) The gas-jar is standing _____ a trough.
c) There is some oxygen _____ the gas-jar.
d) . . . of the gas-jar there is a stand.
e) . . . of the stand there are two clamps which hold a test-tube.
f) _____ the test-tube and the gas-jar there is a tube.
g) . . . the stand there is a base.
h) The base is _____ the test-tube.
i) There is a tripod and a bunsen burner . . . the stand.
j) The burner is _____ the tripod.
k) The gas comes from a tap which is . . . of the tripod.
l) . . . the burner there is a flame.
m) _____ the apparatus there is a conical flask.
n) _____ the conical flask there is a beaker.
o) There is a light _____ the stand.
p) The light is . . . of a wire.
q) The light is _____ the apparatus and the flasks.
r) The apparatus and the flasks are _____ the bench.

15

Section 3 Geographical positions

7. Look at this map of the world and the sentences below it:

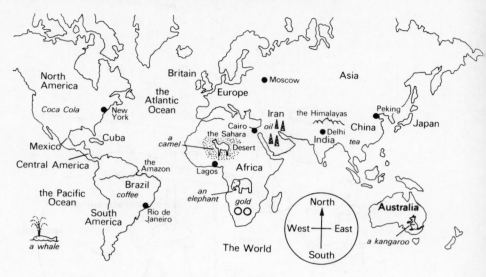

Mexico *is situated in* North America.

Central America is situated *between* North America and South America.

Europe is situated *to the west of* Asia.

The Sahara Desert *is located* in Africa and *to the south-west of* Cairo.

Gold *is found in the south of* Africa.

Kangaroos are found in Australia.

People *are distributed throughout* the world.

Answer these questions:

    a) Where are whales found?
    b) Where is the River Amazon located?
    c) Where is Lagos situated?
    d) Where is the Atlantic Ocean in relation to Europe and North America.
    e) Where are the Himalayas located in relation to China?
    f) Where is tea found?
    g) Where is Moscow situated in relation to Delhi?
    h) Where is India situated in relation to Asia?

Ask and answer some more questions like these.

Write six sentences about your own country, using these words:

is/are situated	is/are distributed throughout
is/are located	to the east of
is/are found	in the north of

16

Section 4 Some parts of objects and their properties

8. Look and read:

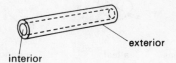

The *interior* of a glass tube is *hollow*.
The *exterior* is hard and smooth.

Ask and answer questions with the words below:

Example: Which part of an egg is hard?
The exterior of an egg is hard.

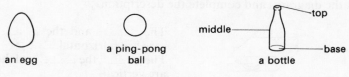

hard/soft   hollow/tough   hard and transparent/
flat/circular/cylindrical/
hollow

Look and read:

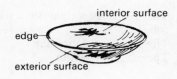

The interior surface of this dish is
concave.
The exterior surface is *convex*.
The *edge* is circular.

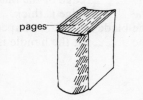

This book is *thick*.
The pages are *thin*.
The edges of the pages are straight.

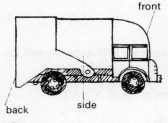

The *front* of this lorry is curved.
The *back* and the *sides* are flat.

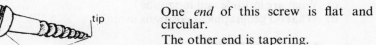

One *end* of this screw is flat and
circular.
The other end is tapering.
The *tip* is *pointed*.

Now ask and answer more questions:

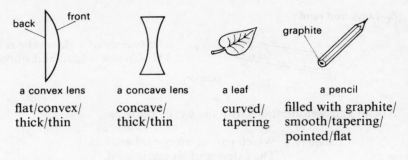

a convex lens	a concave lens	a leaf	a pencil
flat/convex/ thick/thin	concave/ thick/thin	curved/ tapering	filled with graphite/ smooth/tapering/ pointed/flat

Look at the diagrams and complete the descriptions:

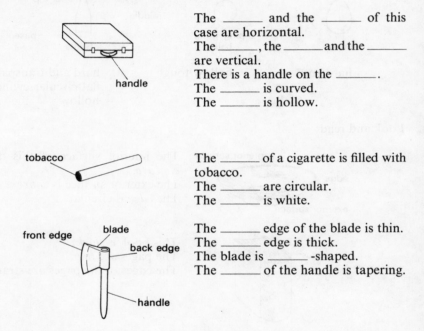

The _____ and the _____ of this case are horizontal.
The _____, the _____ and the _____ are vertical.
There is a handle on the _____.
The _____ is curved.
The _____ is hollow.

The _____ of a cigarette is filled with tobacco.
The _____ are circular.
The _____ is white.

The _____ edge of the blade is thin.
The _____ edge is thick.
The blade is _____ -shaped.
The _____ of the handle is tapering.

Section 5   Reading

9. Look at these questions, then read the text. Which paragraph answers each question?

a) Why are geographical positions given in degrees?
b) What are the tropics?
c) What are latitude and longitude?
d) What do geographical positions mean?

Latitude and longitude
The position of places on the Earth's surface are given in latitude and

18

longitude. These are imaginary circles running round the Earth. Lines
of latitude run horizontally and are parallel to the Equator. Lines of
longitude run vertically. They converge at the North and South
5 Poles.

The position of Chicago is 42°N and 88°W. This means that it is
situated at the point where latitude 42 crosses longitude 88. 'N' means
north of the Equator. 'W' means west of the zero meridian. This is the
line of longitude which passes through Greenwich.

10 Positions are given in degrees. Imagine a line from the centre of the
Earth to the Equator and another line from the centre of the Earth to
Chicago. The angle between these lines is 42°. Similarly, the angular
distance between the zero meridian and Chicago is 88°.

The Earth is not at right angles to its path round the sun. Therefore
15 the position of the sun in relation to the Earth's surface changes
during the year. Twice a year, on March 21st and September 21st, the
sun is vertically over the Equator. At other times it is vertically over
other latitudes between the tropical zones. These lie between the
Tropic of Cancer (23°27'N)† and the Tropic of Capricorn (23°27'S).
20 The sun is vertically over the Tropic of Cancer on June 21st and
vertically over the Tropic of Capricorn on December 21st.

† Read '23 degrees, 27 minutes North'.

10. Now work through these exercises:

a) Label these diagrams:

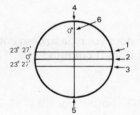 

Equator   Zero meridian   Angle of latitude   Tropic of Cancer
North Pole   Tropic of Capricorn   Angle of longitude   South Pole

b) The position of the South Pole is 90°S. S means .... 90° is the
angle between a line from the Earth's centre to the Equator and
another line from the centre to the ....

c) How do you know that the Tropic of Capricorn is in the southern
hemisphere?

d) Why is it summer in December in the southern hemisphere?

e) Find out your own geographical position and explain what it
means.

Unit 3 Structure

Section 1 Parts and the whole

1. Look and read:

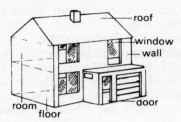

A house *consists of* walls, a roof, floors, doors and windows. (These are the *parts* of the house.)
It *contains* rooms. (The rooms are inside the house.)

Now complete this:

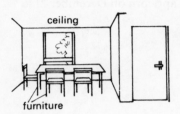

A room _____ walls, a ceiling, a floor, a _____ and _____.
A room often _____ furniture.

Answer these:

What does your classroom consist of?
What does it contain?

Complete this:

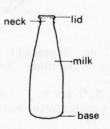

A milk bottle consists of a glass cylinder, a flat _____, a tapering ____ and a lid.
It contains _____.

Answer these:

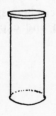

What does a gas-jar consist of?
What does it contain?

20

Complete this:

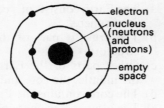

An atom of carbon consists of . . . .
It contains a _____ in the centre.
The nucleus consists of _____ and _____.

2. Read this:

The rooms in a house *include* a bedroom, a sitting-room *etc.* (These are some of the different kinds of room.)

Complete these:

The rooms in a school include . . .

Furniture includes . . .

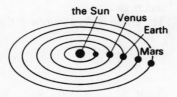

The solar system _____ the Sun and planets. Planets _____ the Earth, Mars, Venus _____.

Look and complete:

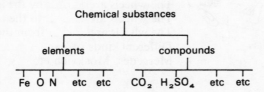

Chemical substances consist of _____ and _____.
Elements include . . . .
Compounds include . . . .

Now read the text and copy out the complete diagram:

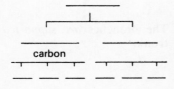

Matter consists of organic substances and inorganic substances.
Organic substances include coal and oil. Inorganic substances include iron and sulphur. Organic substances contain carbon. Inorganic substances do not contain carbon.

21

3. Say whether these statements are true or false. Correct the false statements.

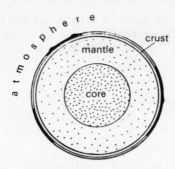

a) The Earth consists of a core and an atmosphere.
b) The crust is part of the Earth's structure.
c) Other parts of the Earth include the mantle, the core and the Sun.
d) The core contains the Earth.
e) The atmosphere contains gases.

Section 2   The connection between parts

4. Look and read:

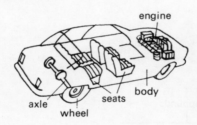

The rectangle *is connected to* the square *by* the line.
The triangle *is attached to* the rectangle.
The circle *is detached from* the square.

Now complete these:

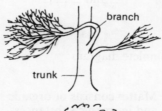

A car _____ a body, seats, an engine, wheels, axles.
The front of this car _____ the engine.
The wheels are _____ by the axles.
The wheels are _____ to the axles.
The wheels are _____ from the body.
Different kinds of car _____
Mercedes, Moskvich etc.

Look and read:

The branch of the tree *is joined to* the trunk.

The branches *are supported by* the trunk.

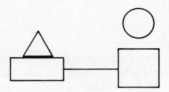

22

Now complete this description:

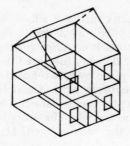

This house consists of . . .
It contains
The rooms include . . . .
The roof is supported by . . . .
The walls are attached to . . . .
This house is shaped like . . . .
The windows are situated . . . .

5. Look and read:

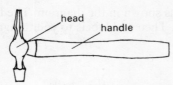

The head of the hammer *is fixed to* the handle. (It cannot move.)

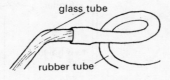

The rubber tube *is fitted over* the glass tube.

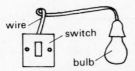

The wire *leads from* the switch *to* the bulb.

Now describe the following objects, using the words given:

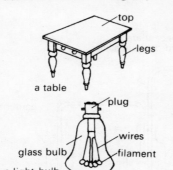

a table

consists of/fixed/supported/top . . . shaped

consists of/contains/shaped/attached/ connected

a light bulb

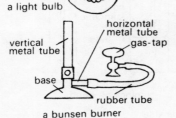

a bunsen burner

consists of/situated/connected/leads from . . . to/fitted over/fixed/shaped

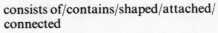

6. Read this text:

The apparatus for preparing hydrogen consists of a flask, a gas-jar, a beehive shelf, a trough, a delivery tube and a thistle funnel. The flask is spherical and has a flat bottom. It contains zinc and hydrochloric acid. The thistle tube and the delivery tube are fitted into the neck of the flask. They are held in place by a two-holed cork. The thistle tube leads down to the hydrochloric acid. The delivery tube leads from the flask to the hole in the beehive shelf. The beehive shelf is placed in the middle of the trough. The trough contains water. The gas-jar is supported by the beehive shelf. Hydrogen is collected at the top of the gas-jar.

Now draw the apparatus, using the parts shown in the diagram. The flask and the trough are in the right position. Then add labels to your diagram.

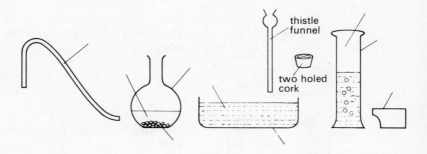

7. Now look at this diagram:

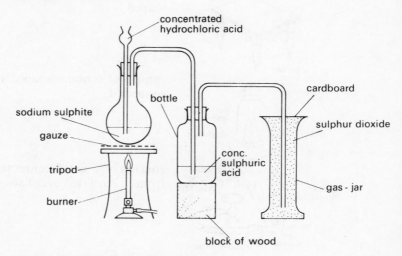

Apparatus for preparing sulphur dioxide

Describe the apparatus as fully as possible, using these words:

> consists of/situated/on the left/in the middle/on the right/supported by/placed under/there is . . . between . . . /fitted into/held in place by/contains/leads down into/leads from . . . to . . .

Section 3 Composition

8. Look at these examples:

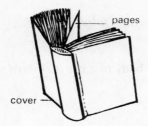

A book consists of pages and a cover.
It contains words and pictures.
The pages *are made of* paper and the cover is made of paper or cardboard.

Now make questions and answers about the following objects:

Example: What does a hammer consist of?
It consists of a head and a handle.
What is it made of?
It is made of metal and wood.

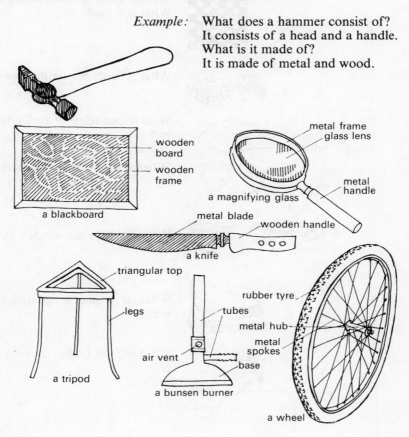

9. Look and read:

This square *is divided into* triangles.

The circle *is surrounded by* stars.

The tyre *is filled with* air.

The body of a car *is covered with* paint.

Now answer these questions:

What is a chess-board divided into?
What is it made of?

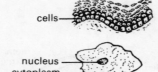

cells

What is living matter divided into?

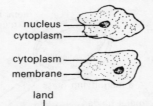

nucleus
cytoplasm

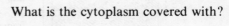

What is the nucleus of a cell surrounded by?

cytoplasm
membrane

What is the cytoplasm covered with?

land

lake

What is a lake surrounded by?

What is a cheese sandwich filled with?

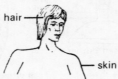

hair

skin

What are our bodies covered with?

26

10. Look at this diagram:

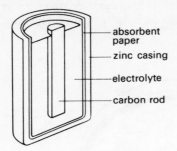

absorbent paper

zinc casing

electrolyte

carbon rod

Now say whether these statements are true or false. Correct the false statements.

a) The diagram shows a dry cell in cross-section.
b) A dry cell is cylindrical in shape.
c) The electrolyte is situated in the centre of the cell.
d) The carbon rod is surrounded by the electrolyte.
e) The thin layer between the casing and the electrolyte is made of paper.
f) The cell is covered with absorbent paper.
g) The biggest part of the cell is filled with electrolyte.

Section 4   Reading

11. Read this text. Then say which of these titles is most suitable and why:

The Earth's crust	**The contents of the Earth**
The properties of the Earth	**The structure of the Earth**

The Earth is a solid sphere. It is made up of three concentric spheres or layers. These are called the core, the mantle, and the crust. The solid sphere is surrounded by a gaseous sphere, which is called the atmosphere.

5   We know most about the crust of the Earth which is the outermost sphere. This layer is very thin compared with the diameter of the whole Earth. It is only about 10 km thick under the ocean and about 30 km thick on land. It consists of rock which contains a lot of minerals. These are usually in compounds called oxides, containing
10   oxygen, or sulphides, containing sulphur.

The mantle is much thicker than the crust. It is about 300 km thick. It consists mainly of rocks, but we do not know much about their composition.

The core, which is situated inside the mantle, seems to be divided
15   into two parts. The inner core is about 2800 km in diameter. We believe that it is mainly composed of iron, but it also contains about 10 % nickel. The layer surrounding the inner core is called the outer core and is approximately 2000 km thick. It is probably composed of

molten iron and nickel. However, the metals in the inner core seem to
20 be rigid, and therefore solid. This is because they are under very high
pressure, which causes solidification in spite of the high temperatures
at the centre of the Earth.

Label this diagram:

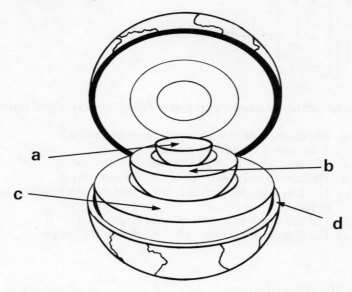

a

b

c

d

12. Say whether these statements are true or false and give reasons:

a) The core is spherical in shape.
b) We know more about the composition of the crust than the
   composition of the mantle.
c) The crust consists of minerals.
d) Iron oxide contains sulphur.
e) The inner core is situated at the centre of the Earth.
f) The outer and inner cores consist of iron.
g) We know that the inner core is solid while the outer core is liquid.
h) At the centre of the Earth, temperature and pressure are both very
   high.

13. Read these notes. Then make similar notes about the other parts of the Earth.

Name: inner core
Location: at centre of earth
Measurement: diameter approx. 2800 km
Composition: solid iron and nickel
Other properties: very hot, high pressure, rigid

Unit A   Revision

1. Look at this diagram:

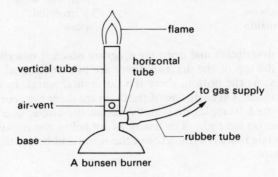

A bunsen burner

Now answer these questions:

Which parts are
a) hollow?
b) flexible?
c) rigid?
d) round?
e) non-combustible?
f) convex?
g) circular?
h) cylindrical?
i) Which part leads to the gas supply?
j) How is the vertical tube connected to the rubber tube?
k) What shape is the flame?
l) What are the tubes made of?
m) Where is the air-vent?
n) How is the rubber tube attached to the horizontal tube?
o) What properties have the metal and rubber tubes in common?

2. Look at this diagram:

Now describe the diagram in sentences, using the following expressions:

a) at the top of
b) at the bottom
c) in the middle
d) on each side of
e) above
f) inside
g) below
h) over
i) diagonally above
j) in line with
k) inverted

3. Read this description and draw the diagram which it describes:

At the top of the diagram there are two horizontal parallel straight lines. At the bottom there is a horizontal spiral. In the middle there is a circle. On each side of the diagram there is a cross. There are two inverted triangles diagonally above the circle, one on the left, the other on the right. The triangles are below the parallel lines. In each triangle there is a dot. Above the spiral and below the circle there is a square.

4. Read these short descriptions and then draw the objects and say what they are:

a) The front of this object is circular or square in shape. Two arrow-shaped pointers are attached to the centre of the circle or square. The edge of the circle or square is divided into twelve equal sections. The front is usually covered with glass or plastic.

b) This object consists of two flat parts, which are both made of wood, joined to each other at right angles. It is T-shaped.

c) This object consists of a closed tube which contains a red or silver liquid, and is made of glass. The tube is cylindrical in shape, but one end is spherical in shape.

d) This object consists of a beam (a horizontal bar), a vertical support under the middle of the beam and two hemispherical pans, which are attached to the ends of the beams by diagonal bars. At the top of the support, under the beam, there is a triangular fulcrum. The support is fixed to a flat base. In front of the support there is a pointer. The top of the pointer is attached to the beam. The tip is in front of a scale. When the two pans are in line the pointer is vertical and the tip of the pointer is in the middle of the scale.

e) This object is made of wood, metal or plastic and is shaped like a long rectangle. The top and bottom edges are divided into sections by short vertical lines.

f) This object is small and made of metal. One end is flat and circular in shape. There is a V-shaped groove across the middle of the circle. The other part of the object is at right angles to the flat end. It is tapering, with a pointed tip. Around the exterior of the tapering part there is a spiral-shaped groove.

Unit 4   Measurement 1

Section 1   Spatial measurements

1. Read this and replace the words in italics with expressions which you have already learnt:

This block of wood has various properties: for example, it is *shaped like a cube; its material is* wood; the material *burns easily; you cannot see through* it; the block is *difficult to bend,* etc.

2. Now read this:

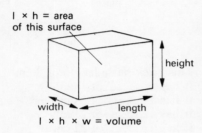

This block has other properties which are measured. It has *height, length* and *width.* Each surface has *area.* The area of the cross-section is the *cross-sectional area.* The area of all the surfaces is the *surface* area. The *volume* of the block = length x height x width (*equals* length *times* height *times* width).

Say which properties of these objects we can measure:

> *Example:*   We can measure the radius, the diameter, the circumference and the area of a circle.

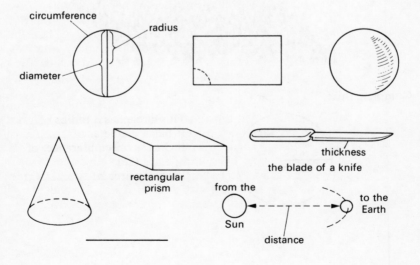

3. Make sentences from the table below. Look in part 1 of the appendix for the names of the units of measurement which are given as abbreviations in the table.

Example: The height of large objects is measured in metres.

| The | height
volume
area
width
surface area
length
radius
cross-sectional area
diameter
circumference | of | large
small
very small
minute
cylindrical | objects | is
measured
in | m
cm
mm
μm
m³
cm³
mm³
m²
cm²
mm² |
| | distance | between | | places | | km |

4. Complete these sentences:

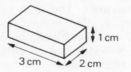

This brick has a length of 3 cm.
It has a _____ of 1 cm.
It has a _____ of 2 cm.
It has a _____ of 2 cm².
It has a _____ of 22 cm².
It has a _____ of 6 cm³.

Describe the measurements of this forest and the trees:

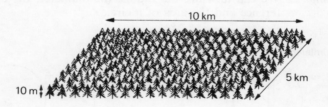

Complete this:

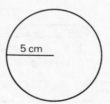

This circle has a radius of _____.
It has a diameter of _____.
It has a circumference of _____. (2πr)
It has an area of _____. (πr²)

Describe the measurements of this coin, including its thickness:

5. Look and read:

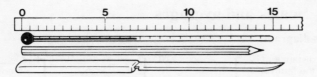

The thermometer has a length of *exactly* 15 cm.
The pencil has a length of *approximately* 15 cm. (exactly 14·9 cm)
The knife also has a length of approximately 15 cm. (exactly 15·2 cm)

Now complete these:

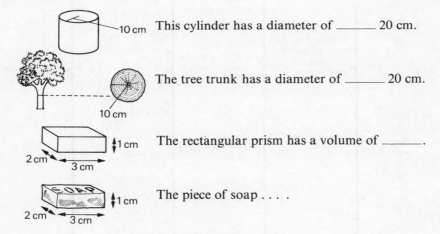

This cylinder has a diameter of _____ 20 cm.

The tree trunk has a diameter of _____ 20 cm.

The rectangular prism has a volume of _____.

The piece of soap . . . .

Section 2   Other measurements

6. Refer to part 2 of the appendix and say whether the following statements are true or false. Correct the false statements.

    a) Duration is measured in degrees Centigrade.
    b) The second is a unit of time.
    c) Speed is measured in kilograms per hour.
    d) The watt is a unit of electrical resistance.
    e) Density is measured in grams per metre cubed.
    f) The gram is a unit of mass.
    g) Liquid measurements are made in litres, or cubic decimetres.

7. Look at part 3 of the appendix and make questions and answers like the following:

> *Example:* What is the speed of light?
> The speed of light is 299,790 km/s.
>
> *or:* The speed of light is approximately 300,000 km/s.

Section 3   Scales and averages

8. Look at this diagram:

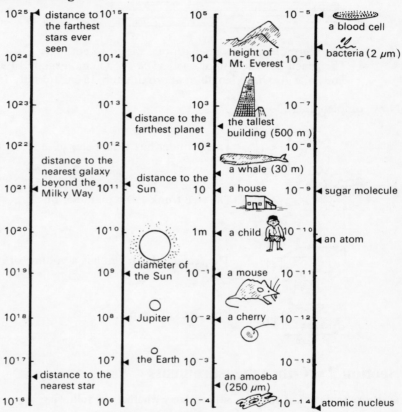

Scale of dimensions (measurements in metres)

Very large and very small quantities are expressed like this:

10^6 = ten *to the power of* six = one million.
10^{-6} = ten *to the power of minus* six = one millionth.

Complete these:

10^2 =   =
10^3 =   =
10^8 =   =
10^{-2} =   =
10^{-5} =   =

9. Refer to part 4 of the appendix and then make sentences like the example about these dimensions:

the distance to the farthest stars, the diameter of the Sun, the diameter of the Earth, the height of Mount Everest, the length of a mouse, the diameter of a cherry, the diameter of a blood cell, the diameter of a sugar molecule

Example: A mouse has a length of approximately ten to the power of minus one metres, ie ten centimetres.

10. Read this:

The above diagram is a *scale* of dimensions. The dimensions *range from* the nucleus of an atom, which has a diameter of approximately 10^{-14} m, *to* the radius of the known universe, which is approximately 10^{25} m.

Now make sentences from the table:

Plants Animals Buildings	range in size from	the whale, the tallest building, the tallest tree,	which	has a	height length	of approximately

500 m, 80 m, 30 m,	to	the amoeba, houses, bacteria,	which	has have	a diameter a height	of approximately	10 m. 250 μm. 2 μm.

11. Look at these histograms:

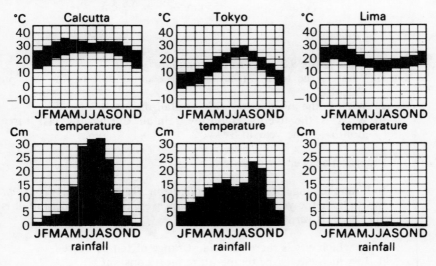

35

Now read this:

The histograms in the top row show the average *range* of temperature (in degrees Centigrade) for each month in three cities. The histograms in the bottom row show their average monthly rainfall (in centimetres).

In Calcutta in January the temperature ranges from 27°C to 13°C; that is, the *maximum* temperature is 27°C and the *minimum* temperature is 13°C. These are the two *extremes* of temperature.

Complete these (see part 5 of the appendix for the names of months):

a) Extremes of temperature in Tokyo in January: maximum _____; minimum _____.
b) In Lima in April the temperature ranges from _____ to _____.
c) Throughout the year in _____ the rainfall ranges from 33 cm to 1 cm.
d) In Tokyo the maximum rainfall occurs in the month of _____, and the minimum rainfall . . . .

Now read this:

The *average* monthly rainfall in Calcutta during the first six months of the year is:

January	1 cm
February	3 cm
March	4 cm
April	5 cm
May	14 cm
June	28 cm
Total	55 cm ÷ 6 = 9·2 cm

Answer these questions:

e) Is the figure 9·2 exact or approximate?
f) What is the total rainfall for the second half of the year in Calcutta?
g) What is the average monthly rainfall during this period?
h) What is the average monthly rainfall during the last three months of the year in Tokyo?

Now read this and answer the questions:

In Lima the range of rainfall is very *narrow*. Rainfall is fairly *constant* throughout the year. In Calcutta, however, the range of rainfall is very *wide*. It *varies* a lot.

i) In which city is there the widest range of temperature?
j) In which city is the temperature most constant?
k) Where does the rainfall vary most?

Section 4 Reading

12. Read the text and find the answers to these questions:

    a) Why did early measurements vary?
    b) How have measurements become more constant?

Standards of measurement

In early times measurements were made by comparing things with
parts of the human body. Early units of measurement included the
distance from the elbow to the fingers, the width of the hand and the
width of the fingers.

5   Some of these human measurements are still used. For example, the
inch is based on the length of half the thumb. A foot was originally the
length of a man's foot. A mile was one thousand walking steps.

    These units were only approximate, because their standard – the
human body – was not constant. Governments tried to standardise
10   them by using rods of fixed lengths. But these rods still varied from
country to country.

    During the French Revolution, scientists looked for a standard of
measurement which did not change. They chose the distance from the
Equator to the North Pole, which is one quarter of the circumference
15   of the Earth. One ten-millionth of this was called one metre and
became the basic unit of the metric system. Other metric units are
based on it. For example, the centimetre is one hundredth of a metre.
A gram – the unit of weight – is the mass of one cubic centimetre of
water.

20   A standard metre was marked on a platinum bar. The accuracy of
measuring instruments was checked by comparing them with this bar.
Nowadays the metre is standardised by comparing it with another
constant – the wavelength of a certain kind of light.

*which is still kept at The ~~French~~
Bureau of
standards,
of The France*

13. Now complete these notes:

    a) ... included the distance from elbow to fingers, width of hand,
        width of finger.
    b) ... include the inch, the foot, the mile.
    c) These ... measurements were not ... because ... . were used
        to standardise them, but these also varied.
    d) ... was chosen as the basic unit of ... . Its length is ... of ... the
        Earth's circumference. Other metric units are ... .
    e) The standard metre is marked on ... . Nowadays another
        constant is used: ... .

Appendix to Unit 4

Part 1   Units of measurement and their abbreviations

kilometre   km
metre   m
decimetre   dm
centimetre   cm
millimetre   mm
square metre m^2
cubic metre m^3
(metre cubed)
micrometre μm = ('micron')

formulae: The area of a circle πr^2
              The circumference of a circle $2\pi r$

Part 2   Other measurements and their units

electric current   ampere (amp)
electric power   watt (W)
electric resistance   ohm (Ω)
electric potential
   difference   volt (V)
temperature   degrees Centigrade ($^\circ$C)
mass   gram (g), kilogram (kg)
weight (the force   newton (N), kilonewton (kN)
   of gravity on
   mass)
speed   kilometres per hour (kph) (kmh^{-1})
density   kilograms per cubic metre (kg/m^3) (kgm^{-3})
time (duration)   second (s), minute (min), hour (hr)
fluid capacity   litre (l) = cubic decimetre (dm^3)

Part 3   Some facts

The speed of light is 299,790 kilometres per second (km/s) (kms^{-1})
The speed of sound in air is 332 metres per second (m/s) (ms^{-1})

Approximate height of mountains:		
	Everest	8,848 m
	Aconcagua	6,960 m
	Kilimanjaro	5,895 m
	Ararat	5,156 m
Approximate length of rivers:	Nile	6,656 km
	Amazon	6,480 km
	Missouri-Mississippi	5,936 km
	Yangtse	5,440 km

Areas and maximum depths of oceans (approximate):

	area	maximum depth
Pacific	102,177,600 km²	12,066 m
Atlantic	50,608,000 km²	9,166 m
Indian	29,996,000 km²	8,800 m

Boiling points:

water	100°C
oxygen	−183°C
alcohol	78°C

Freezing points:

water	0°C
oxygen	−218·4°C
alcohol	−131°C

Density:

gold	19,400 kg/m³
water	1,000 kg/m³
mercury	13,600 kg/m³
alcohol	800 kg/m³

Part 4   Prefixes used in units of measurement

kilo- = x one thousand: 1 km = 1000 m

deci- = one tenth: 1 dm = $\frac{1}{10}$ m $\qquad 10^{-1}$

centi- = one hundredth: 1 cm = $\frac{1}{100}$ m $\qquad 10^{-2}$

milli- = one thousandth: 1 mm = $\frac{1}{1000}$ m $\qquad 10^{-3}$

micro- = one millionth: 1 μm = $\frac{1}{1000000}$ m $\qquad 10^{-6}$

nano- = one thousand millionth: 1 nm = $\frac{1}{1000000000}$ m $\quad 10^{-9}$

Part 5   Months of the year

January	July
February	August
March	September
April	October
May	November
June	December

Unit 5   Process 1   Function and Ability

Section 1   Function

1. Look and read:

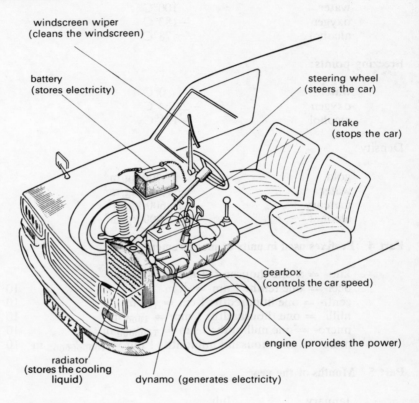

windscreen wiper
(cleans the windscreen)

battery
(stores electricity)

steering wheel
(steers the car)

brake
(stops the car)

gearbox
(controls the car speed)

engine (provides the power)

radiator
(stores the cooling
liquid)

dynamo (generates electricity)

Parts of a car and their functions

Ask and answer questions:

Examples: What *does* the gearbox *do*?
The gearbox *controls* the engine power.

What *is* the gearbox *used for*?
The gearbox *is used for controlling* the engine power.

2. Now write five sentences like the following:

Example: The dynamo *serves to generate* electricity.

40

3. Look and read:

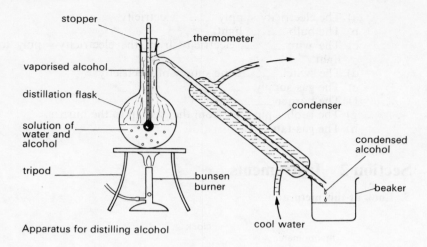

stopper

thermometer

vaporised alcohol

distillation flask

solution of water and alcohol

tripod

condenser

condensed alcohol

bunsen burner

cool water

beaker

Apparatus for distilling alcohol

Now make true sentences from this table:

The function of	the thermometer
	the stopper
	the bunsen burner
	the tube at the top of the
	    condenser
	the cool water
	the tube at the bottom of the
	    condenser
	the beaker
	the tripod
		is to	conduct cool water in.
			heat the liquid.
			collect the condensed alcohol.
			measure the temperature of
			    the solution.
			conduct the cool water away.
			support the apparatus.
			cool the vaporised alcohol.
			hold the thermometer.

4. Look and read:

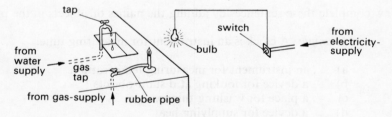

tap

switch

from electricity-supply

from water supply

gas tap

bulb

from gas-supply

rubber pipe

The water-supply *provides* water.
The water-pipe *conducts* water from the water-supply to the tap.
The tap *controls* the supply of water.

Now complete these sentences:

a) The electricity supply _____ electricity.
b) The bulb _____ light.
c) The wire _____ electricity from the electricity-supply to the light.
d) The switch _____ the supply of electricity.
e) The gas-supply _____ gas.
f) The burner _____ heat.
g) The rubber pipe . . . from the gas-tap to the burner.
h) The gas-tap . . . .

Section 2   Instruments

5. Look at this picture:

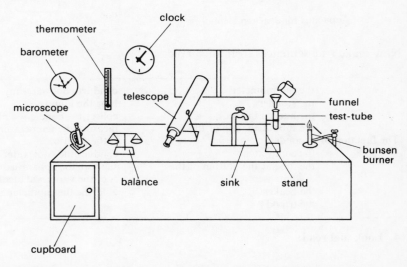

Now complete these sentences by adding the names of objects in the picture:

Example: A clock is an instrument for measuring time.

a) . . . an instrument for measuring temperature.
b) . . . a device for looking at distant objects.
c) . . . a place for washing things.
d) . . . a device for supplying heat.
e) . . . an instrument for weighing things.
f) . . . a device for holding chemicals during experiments.
g) . . . a place for storing things.
h) . . . an instrument for looking at very small things.
i) . . . a device for pouring liquids.
j) . . . an instrument for measuring atmospheric pressure.
k) . . . a device for controlling the supply of water.
l) . . . a device for supporting things during experiments.

6. Look and read:

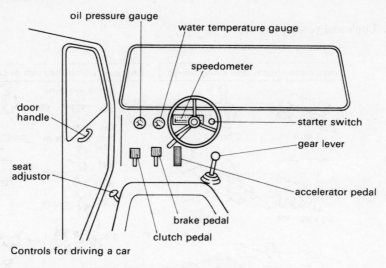

Controls for driving a car

The controls *enable* the driver *to drive* the car.

This means:

With the help of the controls, the driver *can* drive the car.

Now make similar sentences from this table:

The door handle The steering wheel The seat adjustor The gear lever The accelerator pedal The clutch pedal The brake pedal The oil pressure gauge The water temperature gauge The speedometer The starter switch	enables the driver to	check the temperature. stop the car. steer the car. check the oil pressure. change gear. start the engine. check the speed. get in and out. control the speed. adjust the seat. operate the gear lever.

Section 3 Ability and capacity

7. Look and read:

Inanimate objects and living things	Actions which they can or cannot do
a rock a bottle	speak think
an elephant a plane	bite brain
	see
a bat a fish	hear swim
	feel move
a car a plant	walk
	eat divide
a ball a cell	die:
a cloud a bird	grow
	fly
a human being a snake	lift things
	change shape
an amoeba an atom	reproduce
(plural amoebae)	sleep upside down
	breathe
	contain things

Now make questions and answers like the following:

>*Examples:* Can a snake breathe?
>Yes, a snake can breathe.
>
>Can a snake speak?
>No, a snake cannot speak.

8. Make true sentences from this table:

All	animals living things inanimate objects		swim. fly. divide.
Some	human beings cells	can	reproduce. change shape.
No	plants		speak.

9. Look at these examples:

>Plants *can grow.* = Plants *are able to grow.*
>= Plants *have the ability to grow.*
>= Plants *have the capacity to grow.*
>= Plants *are capable of growing.*

Now write full sentences in answer to these questions:

a) What living things are capable of flying?
b) What animals have the capacity to sleep upside down?
c) What living things can swim?
d) What inanimate objects have the capacity to fly?
e) What living things are capable of feeling?
f) What living things have the ability to think?
g) What inanimate objects are capable of changing shape?
h) What living things are able to reproduce?
i) What living things cannot walk?
j) What inanimate objects are capable of moving?

Section 4   Functions in the human body

10. Look and read:

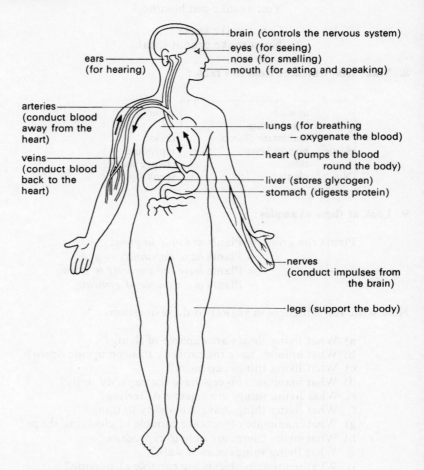

brain (controls the nervous system)
eyes (for seeing)
nose (for smelling)
mouth (for eating and speaking)
ears (for hearing)
arteries (conduct blood away from the heart)
veins (conduct blood back to the heart)
lungs (for breathing – oxygenate the blood)
heart (pumps the blood round the body)
liver (stores glycogen)
stomach (digests protein)
nerves (conduct impulses from the brain)
legs (support the body)

Internal and external parts of the human body
and their functions

Now complete these sentences:

a) Our eyes _____ us _____ see.
b) With the help of our mouths we are _____ to speak and eat.
c) Our ears are organs for _____.
d) With the help of our noses we _____ smell things.
e) Our lungs enable us to _____.
f) The lungs serve to . . . .
g) The _____ of the heart is to circulate the _____.
h) The heart acts as a _____ for the blood.
i) The stomach is used for . . . .

j) The liver is a place for _____ _____.
k) The _____ act as a support for the body.
l) The function of the nerves is to . . . .
m) The function of the brain . . . .
n) The veins . . . .
o) The arteries serve . . . .

Section 5   Reading

11. **Read the text. Then say which of these titles is most suitable and why:**

The
structure
location
functions
properties
of systems in the human body

The human body is made up of a number of different systems. Each
system has a separate function, but some work together. One system is
the skeleton, which serves to support the body and protect the internal
organs. The respiratory system enables us to breathe and take oxygen
5 into the blood, which moves around the body by means of the
circulatory system. The digestive system enables us to take in food
needed for growth. Waste matter is ejected from the body by means of
the urinary system.
    The endocrine system consists of various glands, such as the
10 thyroid, sex and adrenal glands. The function of these glands is to
secrete chemicals, known as hormones, into the blood. These
hormones control various processes in the body, such as growth,
sexual activities and digestion. The nervous system controls the other
systems and enables human beings to think.
15   Each system is made up of organs. The lungs, for example, are part
of the respiratory system. The heart is an organ in the circulatory
system. The liver functions as part of the digestive system and other
systems.
    Every organ is composed of several kinds of tissue. Epithelial tissue,
20 which includes the skin, forms a covering over organs. Connective
tissue supports and holds together parts of the body and includes
bone and cartilage. Other types of tissue include nerve tissue and
blood tissue.
    All tissue consists of cells. These are so small that they are measured
25 in thousandths of a millimetre and can only be seen with a
microscope. Each cell is covered with a thin membrane which
surrounds a nucleus, and a jelly-like substance, called cytoplasm. This
in turn contains minute particles, each with its own special function.

Look at this example. Then make notes about other systems from the first three paragraphs:

Name of system	Function	Its organs include ...
respiratory system	breathing, taking oxygen into the blood	the lungs

12. Describe the following, with the help of the words in brackets:

    a) An organ ...   (structure)
    b) Epithelial tissue ...   (function)
    c) Connective tissue ...   (function)
    d) Tissue ...   (structure)
    e) Cells ...   (measurement)
    f) A cell ...   (structure)
    g) Cytoplasm ...   (property)

Unit 6   Process 2 Actions in Sequence

Section 1   Preceding, simultaneous and following events

1. Look and read:

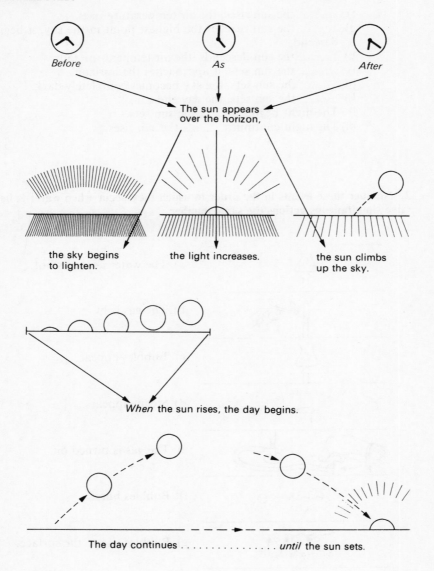

Before

As

After

The sun appears over the horizon,

the sky begins to lighten.

the light increases.

the sun climbs up the sky.

When the sun rises, the day begins.

The day continues . . . . *until* the sun sets.

Each sentence contains two events, X and Y. Read out the sentence which means:

a) X occurs at the same time as Y (simultaneously with Y).
b) X occurs at approximately the same time as, or soon after, Y.
c) X precedes Y.
d) X follows Y.
e) Y is at the end of X.

Now complete these sentences:

f) _____ the sun rises, the air temperature rises.
g) _____ the sun reaches the highest point in the sky, it begins to descend.
h) _____ the sun descends, the air temperature falls.
i) _____ the sun sets, it approaches the horizon.
j) _____ the sun sets, the sky becomes completely dark.
k) _____ the sun sets, the day ends.
l) The night begins _____ the sun sets.
m) The night continues _____ the sun rises.

2. Number these events in the order in which they occur when water is heated. Give simultaneous actions the same number.

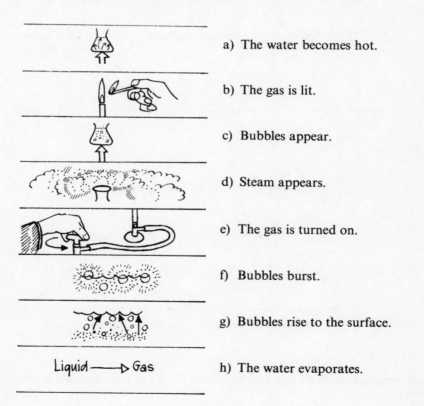

a) The water becomes hot.

b) The gas is lit.

c) Bubbles appear.

d) Steam appears.

e) The gas is turned on.

f) Bubbles burst.

g) Bubbles rise to the surface.

h) The water evaporates.

50

Now look at the two points in this example:

> *As soon as* the gas is turned on, *it* is lit.
> (X follows Y immediately)

Complete these sentences:

    i) As the water evaporates, ...
    j) As soon as the bubbles burst, ...
    k) When the bubbles rise to the surface, ...
    l) As soon as the gas is turned on, ...
    m) Before the gas is lit, ...
    n) After the water becomes hot, ...
    o) As soon as the bubbles appear, ...

3. Number these events in the order in which they occur. Give simultaneous actions the same number.

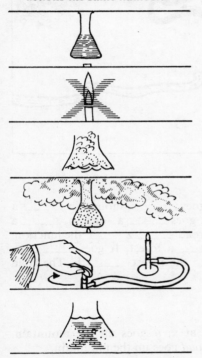

a) The water ceases boiling.

b) The flame is extinguished.

c) The water starts to boil.

d) The water continues boiling.

e) The gas is turned off.

f) The bubbles disappear.

Now write complete sentences joining these pairs of events and making any other necessary changes:

		Use one of these expressions:	
d + *b	*e + b	when	before
*c + d	*a + e	until	after as soon as
*b + a	*a + f		

Example: As soon as the gas is turned off, the flame is extinguished.

Section 2 Sequences

4. Look at this diagram:

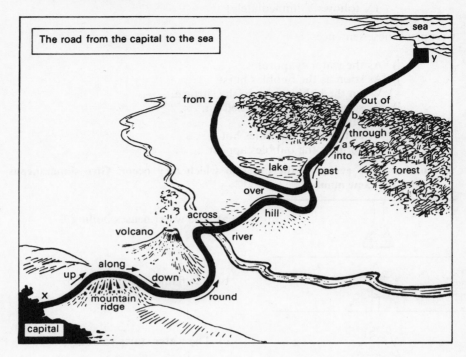

The road from the capital to the sea

Now complete this description:

A road leaves the capital at **x**. It goes _____ a mountain, _____ a ridge and _____ the other side. It goes _____ a volcano, _____ a river and _____ a hill. It joins the road _____ **z** _____ the junction, **j**. It goes _____ a lake and _____ a forest. It goes _____ the forest _____ **a** and comes _____ the forest _____ **b**. The road reaches the sea _____ **y**.

Look at these sentences:

After *the road leaves* the capital at **x**, *it* goes up the mountain.
After leaving the capital at **x**, *the road* goes up the mountain.

When the road reaches **a**, it goes into the forest.
On reaching **a**, the road goes into the forest.

Change these sentences into the second form:

a) After the road goes round the volcano, it crosses the river.
b) Before the road enters the forest, it passes the lake.
c) When the road emerges from the forest, it is near the sea.
d) After the road ascends the hill, it goes along the ridge.

52

e) Before it goes round the volcano, the road descends the mountain.
f) As it goes between the hill and the lake, the road joins the road from z. (*While* going . . .)
g) When the road reaches the volcano, it goes round it.
h) As the road travels from x to y, it crosses a river.

5. Look at this diagram:

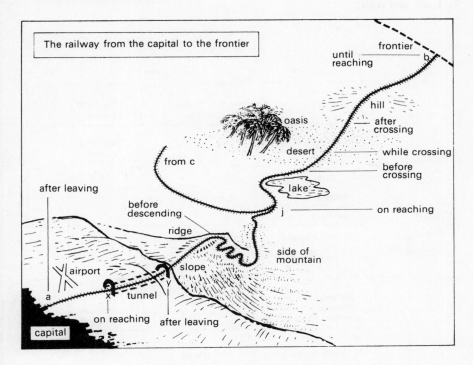

Now write nine sentences using the opening phrases in the diagram.

> *Example:* After leaving the capital at **a**, the railway goes past the airport.

6. Look at these sentences:

> *While crossing* the desert, the railway *passes* an oasis.
> The railway *crosses* the desert, *passing* an oasis.
> (X is simultaneous with Y, or occurs during Y)

Now change these sentences into the second form:

a) While going through the tunnel, the railway passes under the mountain.
b) While descending the mountain, the railway makes several turns.

53

c) While passing the lake, the railway travels in a semi-circle.
d) While crossing the desert, the railway passes an oasis.
e) While approaching the frontier, the railway goes over a hill.
f) While travelling between the mountain and the lake, the railway joins the railway line from **c**.

Section 3   Cycles

7. Look and read:

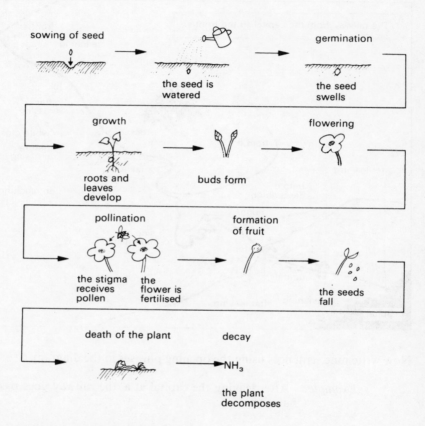

sowing of seed

the seed is watered

germination

the seed swells

growth

roots and leaves develop

buds form

flowering

pollination

the stigma receives pollen

the flower is fertilised

formation of fruit

the seeds fall

death of the plant

decay

NH_3

the plant decomposes

Stages in the life-cycle of a plant

Look at these examples:

Preceding actions:

Before the plant *germinates*, it is watered.
Before ⎱ *germination*, the seed is watered.
Prior to ⎰

Following actions:

After the plant *germinates*, the roots and leaves develop.
After germination, the roots and leaves develop.

Simultaneous actions:

As the plant *germinates*, the seed swells.
During germination, the seed swells.

And this example:

After the seed is watered, *germination* ⎰ *occurs.*
⎱ *takes place.*

Now answer these questions:

a) What happens prior to germination?
b) What occurs during growth?
c) What happens before flowering?
d) What takes place after pollination?
e) What happens after the seeds fall?
f) What occurs before the plant decomposes?
g) What occurs as the plant decomposes?

8. Look at this:

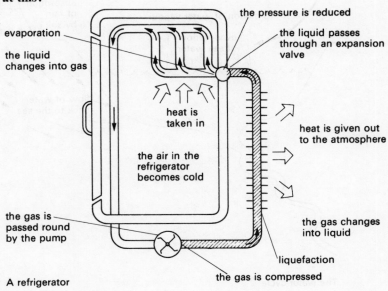

the pressure is reduced

evaporation

the liquid passes through an expansion valve

the liquid changes into gas

heat is taken in

heat is given out to the atmosphere

the air in the refrigerator becomes cold

the gas is passed round by the pump

the gas changes into liquid

liquefaction

the gas is compressed

A refrigerator

Write a description of the cycle of events in a refrigerator, beginning 'As the gas is passed round by the pump, . . .'

9. Look and read:

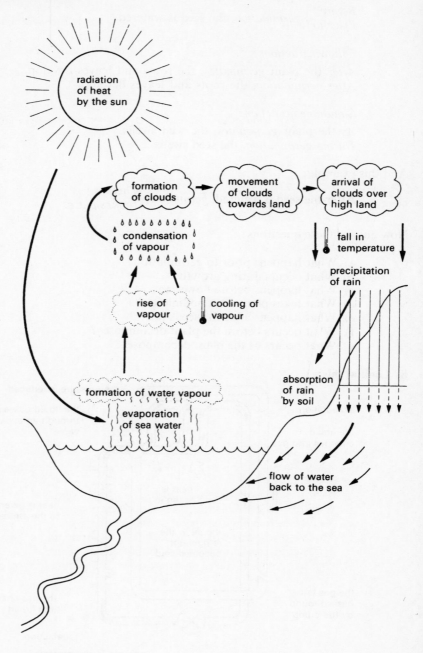

The water cycle

Now write a description of the cycle by joining the correct half-sentences:

When the sun radiates heat,   until they reach high land.
As soon as the water vapour forms,   rain is precipitated.
While rising,   the water flows back to the
                                                  sea.

When the vapour cools,   the vapour cools.
During condensation,   it begins to rise.
The clouds then move towards land,   clouds are formed.
When the clouds reach high land,   it condenses.
As the temperature falls,   sea water evaporates.
On being precipitated,   the air temperature falls.
After being absorbed,   the rain is absorbed by the
                                                  soil.

Section 4   Stages

10. Look again at the life-cycle of a plant and then read this description:

First, the seed is sown.
   Next, it is watered.
      Then, the seed begins to swell.
      At this stage, germination begins.
         Subsequently, the roots develop.
         Meanwhile, the leaves also develop.

   Later, flowers appear.
      Then, pollination takes place.
      During this process, the stigma receives pollen.
         Afterwards, the fruit forms.

            Eventually, the plant dies.
            Finally, the plant decomposes.

The words in *italics* mark stages in a process. Now give the following:

    a) A word which marks the opening, or initial stage.
    b) A word which marks the last, or ultimate, stage.
    c) Two words which mark next or following stages
    d) Three expressions which mark events occurring some time later.
    e) Three expressions which mark simultaneous events.
    f) One word which marks an event occurring after a long process.

11. Put these stages in the right order and then match them with the expressions on the left:

Example: First, the site is bought.

Stages in building a house

First,	the drains are dug.
Then,	the materials are bought.
Meanwhile,	the house is painted.
Subsequently,	the walls are built.
At this stage,	the site is bought.
Next,	the site is levelled.
Afterwards,	the foundations are laid.
Then,	the house is ready to live in.
Later,	the roof is made.
Eventually,	the doors and windows are put in.
Finally,	the electricity and water systems are installed.

Section 5   Reading

12. Look at these questions and then read the text. Which paragraph answers each question?

a) How do animals take in carbon?
b) How is limestone formed?
c) What is the carbon cycle?
d) How do plants take in carbon?
e) How is coal formed?
f) How do animals give up carbon?

The carbon cycle

All plants and animals need carbon for growth. Carbon is present in the atmosphere in the form of carbon dioxide gas. But it is present only in small amounts. This means it has to be used again and again. Animals and plants continually take in and give out carbon during
5 respiration. They also take it in when they feed, and give it out when they die. This continual process is called the carbon cycle.

Plants take in carbon from the air during photosynthesis. In this process, plants use energy from the sun together with carbon dioxide from the air. They then make sugars, and other carbohydrates. The
10 carbohydrates are needed for the growth of roots, stems and leaves.

The leaves may subsequently be eaten by animals, which digest the carbohydrates. The carbon is then used for building muscles and bones. Some of the carbon, however, is returned to the atmosphere after respiration, when carbon dioxide is released from the body.
15   When an animal eventually dies, decomposition of the body tissue takes place. Through the action of bacteria and other organisms, the

chemicals are broken down, or decomposed, and carbon dioxide is
released.

Some dead plants are buried under earth. Over millions of years,
20 the pressure of the earth turns them into coal. When coal is burned to
produce heat, carbon dioxide is released.

Many tiny animals living in the sea have carbon in their shells, in
the form of calcium carbonate. When these animals die, their shells
form layers of calcium carbonate at the bottom of the sea. These
25 eventually turn into a rock, called limestone. After movements of the
earth, the limestone may reach the surface. The wind and rain then
wear away the limestone, and some of its carbon is once more released
into the atmosphere.

13. **Put these labels into the flow-chart:**

CO_2 in atmosphere	animals die
photosynthesis in plants	tissue decomposes
animals eat plants	animals breathe out CO_2
coal	CO_2 given off
	plants buried

Now make your own flow-chart of the formation of limestone.

Unit B Revision

1. Look at this diagram and read the passage which follows:

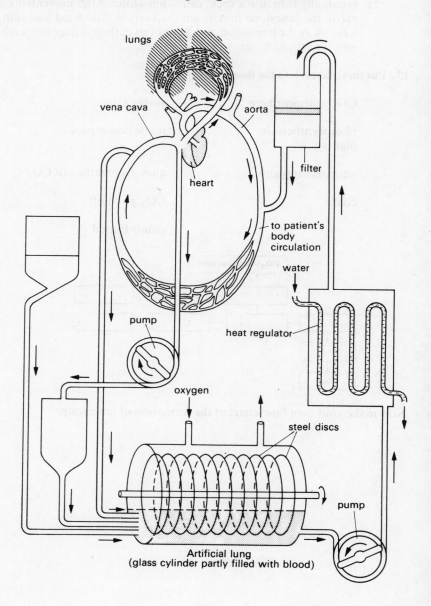

lungs

vena cava

aorta

heart

filter

to patient's
body
circulation

water

pump

heat regulator

oxygen

steel discs

pump

Artificial lung
(glass cylinder partly filled with blood)

The heart-lung machine

The heart-lung machine is used for maintaining the circulation and oxygenation of the patient's blood. It consists of an artificial lung, pumps, tubes and devices for controlling the heat and filtering the blood. The artificial lung serves to oxygenate the blood, which is diverted from the vena cava before reaching the heart.

On leaving the vena cava, the blood enters a plastic tube and flows down this until it enters the artificial lung. This is a horizontal glass cylinder which is partly filled with blood. It contains rotating steel discs. After the blood enters the cylinder it forms a thin film on the surface of the discs. This enables the blood to absorb oxygen, which is pumped through the cylinder. The oxygenated blood subsequently passes through a heat regulator and a filter before returning to the patient's body circulation.

Now answer these questions:

a) What does the artificial lung do to the blood?
b) What is the function of the heat regulator?
c) What does the artificial lung consist of?
d) Why is the blood able to absorb oxygen?
e) Look again at paragraph 2, and complete this chart showing stages in the movement of blood through the heart-lung machine.

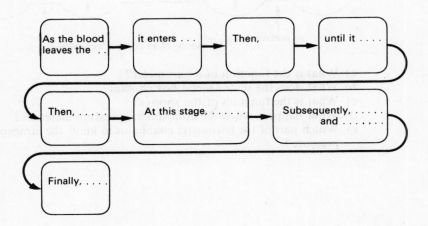

As the blood leaves the .. → it enters ... → Then, → until it .... → Then, ... → At this stage, ... → Subsequently, ... and ...... → Finally, ...

2. Read this passage and answer the questions:

Atmospheric pressure

The average atmospheric pressure at sea-level is approximately 1 kg/cm². This is the pressure which will support a column of mercury (Hg) 760 mm high, and it is called 'one atmosphere'. It is equivalent to the pressure of a column of air approximately 8 km high, if the density of this air is constant and equal to the pressure at sea-level.

a) What is pressure measured in?
b) What is the unit of atmospheric pressure?
c) What is the average pressure of the atmosphere at sea-level?
d) Is atmospheric pressure constant at sea-level or does it vary?
e) How is one atmosphere defined?

3. Read the following paragraph and answer the questions below it:

A barometer is a device for measuring atmospheric pressure. Modern barometers are usually of the aneroid type. This consists of a sealed metal box which has no air in it. The top and bottom of this box are thin plates, which are partly curved and partly flat. In the interior of the box there are springs, which push against the top and bottom plates against external air pressure. When this decreases, the springs can expand but when it increases the springs are compressed. The barometer also contains a pointer joined to the top plate which serves to indicate the change in pressure.

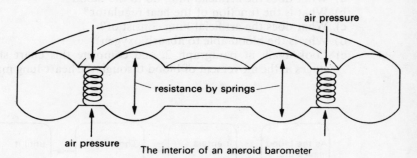

air pressure

resistance by springs

air pressure

The interior of an aneroid barometer

a) What is the function of a barometer?
b) What does the sealed metal box contain?
c) What is the function of the springs?
d) What happens when the atmospheric pressure increases?
e) Which part of the barometer enables us to know the atmospheric pressure?

Unit 7   Measurement 2 Quantity

Section 1   How much and how many?

1. Look at these diagrams:

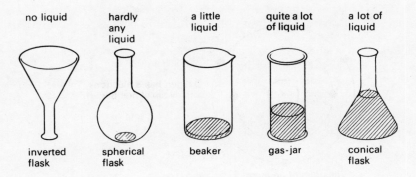

no liquid

hardly any liquid

a little liquid

quite a lot of liquid

a lot of liquid

inverted flask

spherical flask

beaker

gas-jar

conical flask

Make questions and answers like the following:

> *Example:*   How much liquid does the beaker contain?
> It contains a little liquid.

Now look at this:

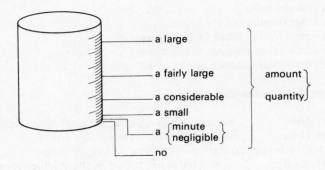

a large

a fairly large

a considerable

a small

a $\begin{Bmatrix} \text{minute} \\ \text{negligible} \end{Bmatrix}$

no

$\begin{rcases} \text{amount} \\ \text{quantity} \end{rcases}$

Note: *Considerable* means large enough to be important.
Negligible means too small to be important.

A lake contains a *very large* quantity of liquid.
The sea contains an *enormous* amount of liquid.

Now write sentences describing the quantities of liquid in the containers above.

2. Look at this:

a few crystals
= a small number
of crystals

quite a few
crystals = a
considerable
number of crystals

many crystals
= a large number
of crystals

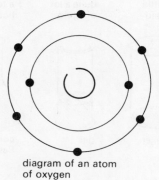

Oxygen has 8 electrons. This is
a fairly small number.

diagram of an atom
of oxygen

Give the names of elements which have, in one atom:

       a few electrons
       a large number of electrons
       a very large number of electrons
       a fairly large number of electrons
       a very small number of electrons

3. Complete these sentences:

a) How _____ electrons does an atom of sodium possess?
b) How _____ oxygen does the atmosphere contain?
c) Our bodies contain a very large _____ of water.
d) A large _____ of whales are found in the Pacific Ocean.
e) There is an _____ number of stars in the universe.
f) For a rich man, one dollar is a _____ quantity of money, but for a poor man it is a _____ amount.
g) The air consists of _____ nitrogen (78 %), _____ oxygen (21 %), _____ argon (less than 1 %) and _____ helium, neon, krypton and xenon.
h) An orange contains _____ seeds.
i) The _____ of bacteria in the air is _____.
j) _____ people can speak more than 5 languages.

4. Look again at the diagrams of the containers (exercises 1 and 2) and read this:

The conical flask contains *much more* liquid than the beaker.
The beaker contains *considerably less* liquid than the gas-jar.
The beaker contains *slightly more* liquid than the spherical flask.
The dish on the right contains *many more* crystals than the dish on the left.
The dish on the left contains *considerably fewer* crystals than the dish in the middle.

Complete these:

a) The conical flask contains . . . than the gas-jar.
b) The spherical flask contains . . . than the beaker.
c) The beaker contains . . . than the conical flask.
d) The dish in the middle contains . . . than the dish on the right.
e) The dish on the right contains . . . than the dish in the middle.

5. Look at these tables:

Elements in the Earth's crust:

		%
Oxygen	(O)	49
Silicon	(Si)	26
Aluminium	(Al)	8
Iron	(Fe)	5
Calcium	(Ca)	3*
Sodium	(Na)	3*
Potassium	(K)	2
Magnesium	(Mg)	2
Titanium	(Ti)	0·63
Hydrogen	(H)	0·13
Phosphorus	(P)	0·13
Manganese	(Mn)	0·10
Sulphur	(S)	0·052
Carbon	(C)	0·032

*approximately equal quantities

Number of electrons in one atom of some metals:

Lithium	(Li)	3
Sodium	(Na)	11
Magnesium	(Mg)	12
Potassium	(K)	19
Manganese	(Mn)	25
Iron	(Fe)	26
Copper	(Cu)	29
Zinc	(Zn)	30
Strontium	(Sr)	38
Tin	(Sn)	50
Gold	(Au)	79
Mercury	(Hg)	80
Lead	(Pb)	82
Radium	(Ra)	88
Uranium	(U)	92

Now make comparisons like the following examples:

The Earth's crust contains much more oxygen than magnesium.
An atom of iron possesses slightly fewer electrons than an atom of copper.

Section 2   Enough and too much

6. Look at this:

These are the *average quantities* of food consumed by *1 person* at the Asia Restaurant:

Meat	125 grams
Rice	150 grams
Bread	100 grams
Onion	1
Tomatoes	2

If the restaurant has the following quantities, calculate how much of each kind of food is available:

Meat	6 kilos
Rice	9 kilos
Bread	5 kilos
Onions	60
Tomatoes	80

Example: There is *enough meat for* 48 people.

a) (Rice)
b) (Bread)
c) (Onions)
d) (Tomatoes)

7. Say whether the supply of each kind of food is adequate or not when exactly 50 people eat at the restaurant.

Example: There is *exactly enough* bread.

a) There is *too much* _____.
b) There are *too many* _____. } (ie more than enough)
c) There is *too little* _____.
d) There are *too few* _____. } (ie not enough)

8. Now look at this:

One day, 55 people come to the restaurant, which has these quantities of food:

Meat	7 kilos
Rice	8·25 kilos
Bread	5 kilos
Onions	50
Tomatoes	120

Write down how *much* (or *many*) of each kind of food there *is* (or *are*) using these words:

a) too little
b) too few
c) exactly enough

d) too much
e) too many

9. Look at these examples:

To be healthy, you must eat
$\begin{cases} \textit{the right quantity of} \\ \textit{enough} \\ \textit{a sufficient amount of} \\ \textit{an adequate amount of} \end{cases}$ food,

but
$\begin{cases} \textit{too much} \\ \textit{an excess of} \\ \textit{an excessive amount of} \end{cases}$ food makes you fat,

and
$\begin{cases} \textit{too little} \\ \textit{a lack of} \\ \textit{an insufficient quantity of} \\ \textit{an inadequate amount of} \end{cases}$ food makes you thin, and hungry.

From your own knowledge, can you say which is the right phrase in each of these sentences?

a) (Too much/a lack of/an excess of) iron causes anaemia.
b) (A lack of/a sufficient quantity of/an excess of) carbohydrate causes fatness.
c) If your food has not (sufficient/excessive/insufficient) calories, you will not have enough energy.
d) (The right quantity/an inadequate amount/an excess) of vitamins is necessary for health.
e) (An adequate amount/an excessive amount/an inadequate amount) of calcium causes bone disease.
f) If you have (an insufficient amount/an excessive amount/ a sufficient amount) of clothing, you will be too hot.
g) If you have (an adequate amount of/an excess of/too little) clothing, you will be too cold.
h) Unless they have (a lack of/ an adequate amount of/an excessive amount of) water, plants will not grow.

10. Look at this example:

Why can't you take a photograph? (light)
Answer: Because the light is insufficient.

Answer the following questions, using these words:

insufficient, inadequate, sufficient, adequate, excessive.

a) Why is the tyre flat?
(air pressure)

e) Why can't the boat go further?
(water)

b) Why has the tyre burst?
(air pressure)

f) Why can't the boat move?
(wind)

c) Why does the light shine brightly?
(current)

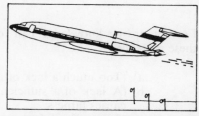

g) Why can the plane leave the ground?
(speed)

d) Why will the boat sink?
(cargo)

Section 3   Too small and big enough

11.   Look at these examples:

Why can't you write your name in this rectangle?   ☐
Answer: Because it's *too small to write in*.

Why can you write it here?   ☐

Answer: Because it's *big enough to write in*.

Now answer these questions (using the words in *italics*):

a) Why can't you *put* an elephant *in your pocket?*

b) Why can't you *touch* the ceiling?

c) Why can't you *lift* a lorry?

d) Why does a cork *float?*

e) Why can't the lorry *go down the street?*
(wide)

f) Why can't you *cut* a diamond?

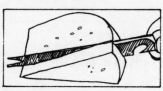

g) Why can you *cut* cheese?

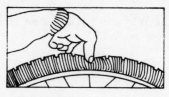

h) Why can you *bend* rubber? (flexible)

i) Why can't you *bend* concrete? (rigid)

j) Why can you *see bacteria* with a microscope? (powerful)

k) Why can't you *see bacteria with* a magnifying glass? (weak)

l) Why can't you *see through* paper? (opaque)

12. Look at this map:

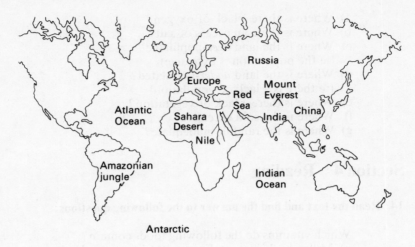

Look at these examples:

> Europe is *too cold for* tea plants.
> Parts of India are *warm enough to grow tea in*.

Now write ten sentences like these examples with *too/enough* and *for* (+ noun) or *to* (+ verb), using these words:

the Antarctic	cold		penguins flowers camels
the Sahara Desert	warm		tea plants
Mount Everest	hot	**for**	bananas
the Atlantic Ocean	dry		apples
the Red Sea	damp		people
Russia	deep		fresh water fish
the River Nile	big		wheat
the Nile valley	wide		
the Amazonian jungle	narrow		walk across
Northern Europe	salty		live in (or on)
China	fertile		visit in one day
etc.	infertile	**to**	grow many plants in
	temperate		drink
	high		irrigate a large area of land
			support a large population
			swim across

71

13. Look at the map again and answer these questions:

a) Where is there a lack of oxygen?
b) Where is there an excess of salt?
c) Where is the land *over*-populated?
   (ie the population is excessive)
d) Where is the land *under*-populated?
   (ie there is a lack of population)
e) Where is there a lack of vegetation?
f) Where is the cold excessive?
g) Where is the rainfall inadequate?

Section 4   Reading

14. Read the text and find the answer to the following questions:

Which vitamins do the following foods contain?
a) Milk   b) Liver   c) Eggs   d) Cheese   e) Fruit
f) Vegetables   g) Fish   h) Oil

Vitamins
Food contains only minute quantities of the substances called
vitamins, but they are vital for good health. For example, if you eat a
diet of meat, bread, sugar and fat, you may become ill with a disease
called scurvy. This is caused by a deficiency in vitamin C, which is
5 found in fruit and vegetables.
About fifty different vitamins have been identified, and a deficiency
in many of these can lead to illness. Vitamin A is most important for
good eyesight, but is also important for general good health. Liver
contains a considerable amount of vitamin A, but vitamin A is also
10 found in fish, meat, milk, butter, some fruits and vegetables.
Vitamin B in fact consists of twelve different chemicals, which are
found in eggs, cheese, butter, wholemeal flour and vegetables. If a
person has an inadequate amount of vitamin B in his diet, this may
affect his whole body, particularly the skin, the nervous system and
15 the heart. Deficiency in vitamin B results in a disease called beri-beri.
Vitamin C prevents scurvy and helps to heal injuries. Some doctors
believe that large quantities of vitamin C help people to avoid colds.
Fruits and uncooked vegetables are rich in vitamin C, but when they
are overcooked, or left for a long time, they lose most of their
20 vitamins.
Vitamin D is essential for the growth of bones and teeth and is
found in fish, liver, oil and milk. Vitamin D is the only vitamin which
the body can make for itself, but it can only do this if there is sufficient
sunlight. A lack of both sunlight and vitamin D can result in a disease
25 called rickets, which causes bones to soften and to be deformed.
Vitamins are only needed in very small quantities. A quantity
sufficient for a whole life would weigh only a quarter of a kilogram.
Vitamins can be manufactured and are sold as additions to our food,
but a well-balanced diet will provide an adequate amount of vitamins.

15. Complete the following table:

Name of vitamin	Foods the vitamin is found in	Results of a deficiency of the vitamin

16. If a person is suffering from the following diseases, which foods will help him?

    a) Scurvy
    b) Rickets
    c) Beri-beri
    d) Poor eyesight
    e) Pellagra (a disease which affects the skin and the nervous system)

Unit 8 Process 3 Cause and Effect

Section 1 Actions and results

1. Look at this example:

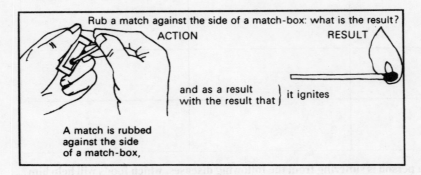

Rub a match against the side of a match-box: what is the result?

ACTION   RESULT

and as a result
with the result that } it ignites

A match is rubbed
against the side
of a match-box,

Now make similar statements about the actions and results below:

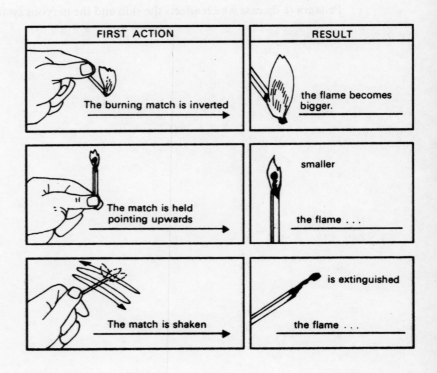

FIRST ACTION	RESULT
The burning match is inverted	the flame becomes bigger.
The match is held pointing upwards	smaller the flame . . .
The match is shaken	is extinguished the flame . . .

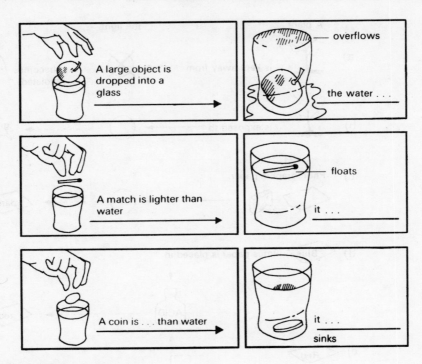

A large object is dropped into a glass →	overflows — the water . . . _____
A match is lighter than water →	floats — it . . . _____
A coin is . . . than water →	it . . . _____ sinks

2. Look at this example:

ash
bubbles
green

Changes of state

The process of smoking a water-pipe: smoke is sucked down the pipe, and as a result the smoke *changes into* bubbles, the water *turns* green and the smoke *becomes* cool. *Another result is that* the tobacco *is converted into* ash.

Make statements about the following actions and resulting changes, using *with the result that* or *and as a result*, and the words *become* (+ adjective), *turn* (+ colour), *change into* or *be converted into* (+ noun).

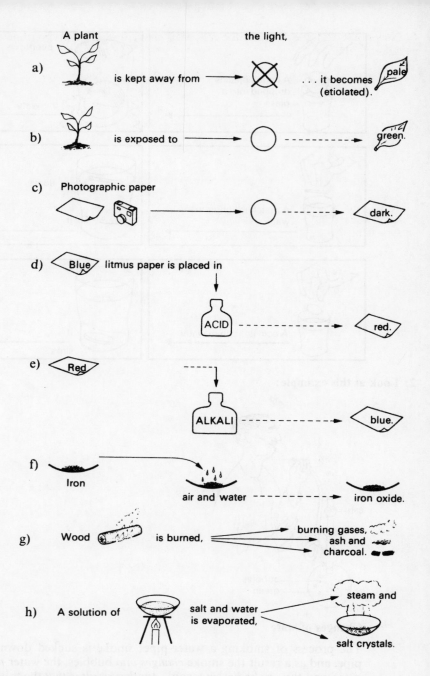

a) A plant is kept away from the light, ... it becomes pale (etiolated).

b) A plant is exposed to the light, green.

c) Photographic paper dark.

d) Blue litmus paper is placed in ACID red.

e) Red ALKALI blue.

f) Iron air and water iron oxide.

g) Wood is burned, burning gases, ash and charcoal.

h) A solution of salt and water is evaporated, steam and salt crystals.

3. Now change the above descriptions of actions and results in the same way as the example:

Example: *If* a plant *is kept* away from the light, it *will become* etiolated.

4. Now make statements about the following changes of state in the same way as this example:

> *Example:* If ice is heated to melting point, it will melt, *changing* into water.

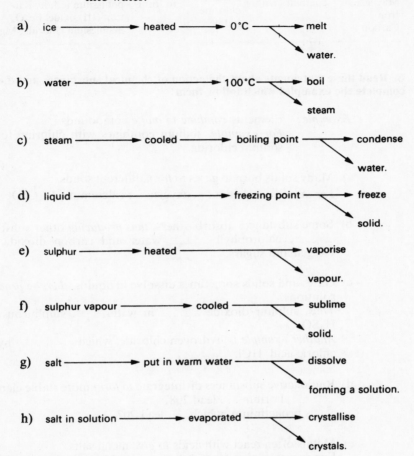

a) ice ———→ heated ———→ 0°C ⟍→ melt
                                     → water.

b) water ———→ 100°C ⟍→ boil
                                → steam

c) steam ———→ cooled ———→ boiling point ⟍→ condense
                                      → water.

d) liquid ———→ freezing point ⟍→ freeze
                                → solid.

e) sulphur ———→ heated ⟍→ vaporise
                                → vapour.

f) sulphur vapour ———→ cooled ⟍→ sublime
                                → solid.

g) salt ———→ put in warm water ⟍→ dissolve
                                → forming a solution.

h) salt in solution ———→ evaporated ⟍→ crystallise
                                → crystals.

Section 2   Other ways of expressing results

5. Look at this:

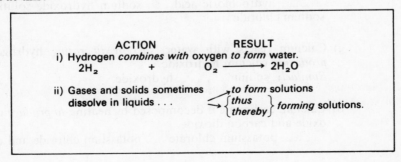

```
            ACTION              RESULT
i) Hydrogen combines with oxygen to form water.
   2H₂          +      O₂ ——→  2H₂O

ii) Gases and solids sometimes    → to form solutions
    dissolve in liquids . . .    ⟍ { thus    } forming solutions.
                                   { thereby }
```

Make sentences describing chemical reactions from this table:

Potassium Calcium Magnesium Iron Carbon	combines with	hydrogen oxygen chlorine iodine	to form	calcium oxide, CaO. methane, CH_4. potassium iodide, KI. iron (III) oxide, Fe_3O_4. magnesium chloride, $MgCl_2$.

6. Read these statements about the action of chemical substances and then complete the examples which follow them:

Example: Elements *combine to make* compounds.
For example, sodium combines with chlorine to form sodium chloride.

a) Many solids burn in gases *to form* different solids.
For instance, calcium . . . oxygen . . . calcium oxide, CaO.

b) Some substances absorb others, *thus producing* other substances.
_____, chlorophyll _____ water and carbon dioxide, . . . oxygen and sugars.

c) Gases and solids sometimes dissolve in liquids, *thereby producing* solutions.
Thus, sulphur dioxide _____ in water, . . . sulphurous acid, H_2SO_3.
Another example is hydrogen chloride, which . . . , . . . hydrochloric acid, HCl.

d) Radioactive substances disintegrate *to form* more stable elements.
_____, thorium . . . lead 208.
. . . is proactinium, which . . . lead 207.

e) Metals often react with acids *to give* metal salts.
For example, zinc . . . sulphuric acid . . . zinc sulphate, $ZnSO_4$.

f) An acid is neutralised by an alkali *to form* a salt.
_____, hydrochloric acid . . . sodium hydroxide solution . . . sodium chloride.

g) Calcium reacts with water, *thereby liberating* hydrogen and *producing* calcium hydroxide.
Similarly, sodium . . . , . . . hydroxide.

h) Calcium carbonate is decomposed by heating *to produce* calcium oxide and carbon dioxide.
_____, potassium chlorate . . . potassium chloride and oxygen.

7. Read this passage and look at the diagram:

The carbon cycle
The life of plants and animals depends on chemical substances containing carbon atoms. Plants obtain carbon from the very small amounts of carbon dioxide in the atmosphere. This atmospheric CO_2 is continually absorbed and given off (released) in the 'carbon cycle'.

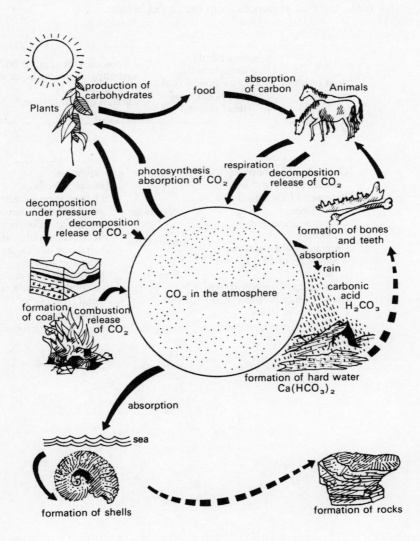

Look at these:

(A = cause, B = result)

A *results in* B.
B *results from* A.
As a result of A, B occurs.
A *leads to* B (eventually: other events occur between A and B).

Now make ten true sentences from the tables below:

	eating plants, photosynthesis, combustion of coal, decomposition of dead plants,	carbon dioxide is given off. carbohydrates are produced by plants. animals absorb carbon.
As a result of		

| Decomposition of plants under pressure
Release of CO_2 into the atmosphere
Decomposition of dead animals
Formation of hard water
Absorption of CO_2 by the sea
Production of carbohydrates
Formation of carbonic acid
Formation of shells | results in

results from

leads to | respiration.
photosynthesis.
the formation of teeth and bones in animals.
the formation of rocks.
the formation of coal.
the release of CO_2 into the atmosphere.
the formation of shells.
the combination of rain and CO_2 in the atmosphere. |

Section 3　Causing, allowing, preventing

8. Rea_·l this sentence and look at the diagrams:

A valve *allows* liquid *to flow* one way and *prevents* it *from flowing* the other way.

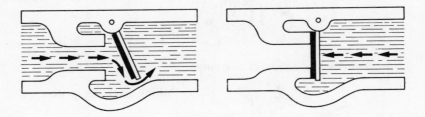

Answer these questions:

    a) Can the liquid flow from left to right?
    b) Why?
    c) Can the liquid flow from right to left?
    d) Why not?

Look at the diagram of the heart and make two sentences about the function of the valves, using the words given:

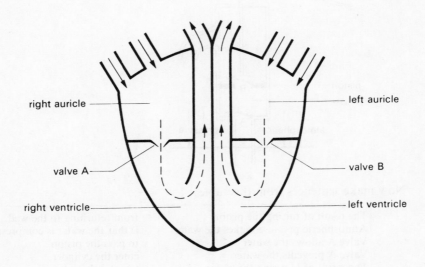

    e) Valve A allows blood/from/to/but prevents/from/to.
    f) Valve B . . . .

9. Read these sentences:

Sucking air up a tube *causes* the air pressure *to decrease*, with the result that it becomes lower than the atmospheric pressure.

Atmospheric pressure *consequently makes* the water *enter* the tube

Now describe the action of a syringe:

piston

Pulling back the piston. . . .

10. Look at this diagram of a lift pump:

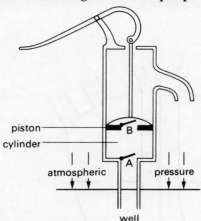

piston

cylinder

B

A

atmospheric   pressure

well

Now make sentences from this table:

The result of raising the piston	from returning to the well.
Atmospheric pressure makes the water	is that the water is compressed.
Valve A allows the water	to pass the piston.
Valve A prevents the water	enter the cylinder.
The result of lowering the piston	to enter the cylinder.
Compression makes the water	from returning past the piston.
Valve B allows the water	is that the air pressure is reduced.
Valve B prevents the water	pass the piston.

11. Look and read:

The effects of heat

These are observable changes produced by heating; some of them
help chemists to identify substances:

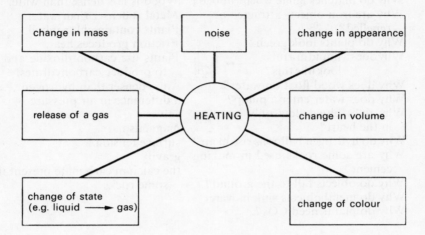

Now make pairs of sentences like the following. Use your own knowledge
of chemistry, or use previous examples from this unit, or think of the
effects of cooking:

Example: Heating $\begin{cases} produces \\ brings\ about \\ causes \end{cases}$ a change of state in ice.

        It *causes it to* melt.

Section 4 Explanations

12. Look at this example:

Why do matches ignite when rubbed?

Matches ignite when rubbed $\nearrow\searrow$ $\begin{cases} because\ of \\ owing\ to \end{cases}$ → friction.
                                           because friction generates heat.

Now write explanations in answer to the following questions. The sentences
and phrases on the right will help you. Choose between *because* and *because
of/owing to*.

Note: Do not repeat the noun after *because*; use a pronoun (it/they)

Example: Wood floats on water because *it* is less dense than water.

Questions	Reasons/causes
Why do matches ignite when rubbed?	Wood is less dense than water.
Why are iron objects attracted or repelled?	Metal is denser than water.
	Plants contain chlorophyll.
Why do plants look green?	Friction produces heat.
Why does a liquid in a tube look like this?	Plants use carbon dioxide and water to produce carbohydrates.
Why does wood float on water?	Air is denser than hydrogen.
Why does water enter a pump?	a difference in air pressure
Why does blood flow only one way in the heart?	valves
	magnetism
Why do hydrogen balloons rise in air?	surface tension
Why are some rocks used in making cement?	gravity
	the calcium carbonate present in some rocks
Why do objects fall to the ground?	
Why do metal objects sink in water?	
Why do plants need CO_2?	

13. Now make some statements like the following pair of sentences, using
therefore **or** *consequently*:

Example: Plants contain chlorophyll. $\left.\begin{array}{l}\textit{Therefore,}\\ \textit{Consequently,}\end{array}\right\}$ they look green.

Section 5   Reading

14. Read this text. Which paragraph answers each question?

   a) How does a thermostat work?
   b) How is central heating controlled?
   c) What causes expansion and contraction?
   d) What is the function of a thermostat?

Thermostats
Heat causes substances to expand. This is because heat causes the atoms and molecules in the substance to move more quickly. As a consequence, they take up more space. This is true for gases, liquids and solids, but gases expand much more than liquids, and liquids
5 much more than solids. When a substance is cooled, the molecules slow down and as a result the substance contracts.
     Thermostats make use of the principle of expansion. The function of a thermostat is to maintain a constant temperature over a period of time. They are used in refrigerators, heating and cooling systems and
10 many industrial processes.

When different materials are heated, some expand more than others. For example, if brass is heated by one degree Celsius, it will expand by one fifty-thousandth of its length. Heating copper, on the other hand, will cause it to expand by about 90 % of this. One kind of
15 thermostat contains a strip of brass and a strip of copper which are joined to form a 'bimetallic strip'. When the strip is heated, the different metals expand by different amounts. As a result, the strip is forced to bend towards the side which expands less. This bending can be used to operate a valve or open and close an electrical circuit.
20   Such a bimetallic strip is used in central heating systems. It switches off the heaters when the air reaches a certain temperature, and switches them on when the temperature falls. One end of the strip can move while the other is fixed. The free end completes an electrical circuit which controls the gas or oil burner. The strip bends as it is
25 heated. At a certain temperature the strip bends sufficiently to break the contact, thereby switching off the burner. When the air cools, the strip contracts until it makes contact and switches the burner on again.

15. Match these diagrams with different parts of the passage and discuss them:

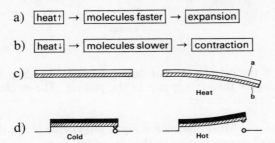

a) heat↑ → molecules faster → expansion

b) heat↓ → molecules slower → contraction

c)

d)

16. Say whether these statements are true or false and explain your answer:

a) The molecules in gases can move further than the molecules in liquids and solids.
b) Only gases expand when heated.
c) If copper is heated by one degree Celsius, it will expand by about one forty-five thousandth of its length.
d) A bimetallic strip made of copper and brass will bend towards the copper side.
e) Substances contract by different amounts when cooled.
f) When a refrigerator gets warmer, its cooling system is switched on by means of a thermostat.

Unit 9   Measurement 3   Proportion

Section 1   Relative size

1. Look and read:

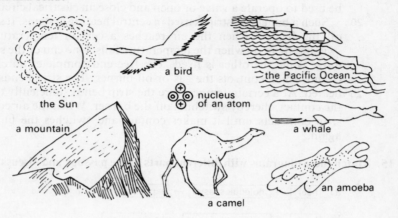

the Sun

a bird

the Pacific Ocean

nucleus
of an atom

a mountain

a whale

a camel

an amoeba

The things in the picture are not drawn *to scale*. The Sun is in fact very much bigger than it appears in the picture. The nucleus of an atom is very much smaller.

Sizes are *relative*. Most objects are big *in proportion to* the size of an atom but small in proportion to the size of the Sun.

Make sentences like the following:

> *Example:*   A camel is big in proportion to the size of an amoeba but small in proportion to the size of a mountain.

2. Now make questions and answers like the following:

> *Example:*   Is a mountain large or small?
> *Compared with* the size of the Sun, a mountain is *relatively* small.

3. Read this:

> The length of the river Nile: 6,656 km
> The height of Mount Everest: 8,848 m
> The population of New York: 11,528,649

Now make sentences about rivers, mountains and cities in your country, like this:

Compared with
$\begin{Bmatrix} \text{(river)}, & \text{(river)} \\ \text{(mountain)}, & \text{(mountain)} \\ \text{(city)}, & \text{(city)} \end{Bmatrix}$
is relatively $\begin{cases} \text{high,} \\ \text{long,} \end{cases}$
has a relatively large population,

but compared with $\begin{cases} \text{the Nile,} \\ \text{Everest,} \\ \text{New York,} \end{cases}$ it is relatively $\begin{cases} \text{low.} \\ \text{short.} \\ \text{small.} \end{cases}$

4. Now look at this bar-graph:

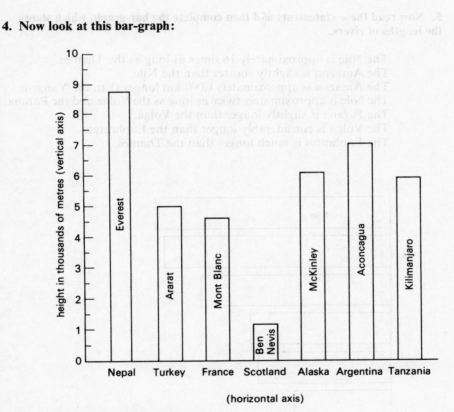

The relative heights of Mountains

Read and complete this:

The rectangles show the heights of different mountains.
The heights are marked on the _____ axis. The scale is shown in thousands of _____. The heights of these mountains range from _____ to _____.

87

Now compare the heights of the mountains, making sentences from the two tables below:

Example: Everest is nearly nine times as high as Ben Nevis.
Aconcagua is considerably higher than Mont Blanc.

nearly approximately	the same height as . . . twice as high as . . . x times as high as . . .	
much considerably slightly	higher lower	than . . .

5. Now read these statements and then complete the bar-graph, which shows the lengths of rivers.

The Nile is approximately 16 times as long as the Thames.
The Amazon is slightly shorter than the Nile.
The Amazon is approximately 1,000 km longer than the Yangtse.
The Nile is approximately twice as long as the Volga and the Parana.
The Parana is slightly longer than the Volga.
The Volga is considerably longer than the Euphrates.
The Euphrates is much longer than the Thames.

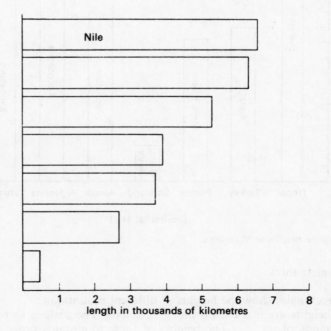

length in thousands of kilometres

Section 2 Percentages and ratios

6. Look and read:

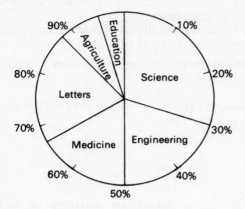

This chart shows the relative numbers of students in different faculties of a university. You can see that *the majority* (the greater part) of students study scientific or technical subjects, whereas students of letters are *in the minority*.

The proportions are approximate. They can be expressed as *percentages*. Thus, science students *constitute* approximately 30% (thirty per cent) of all students.
(Note: A consists of B = B constitutes A.)

Now complete these statements:

a) Engineering students . . . of all students.
b) 50% of all students study _____ or _____.
c) The _____ of students in the faculties of engineering and letters are approximately the same.
d) There are _____ few students of education.
e) _____ the percentage of science students, the percentage of agriculture students is relatively small.
f) In the faculty of science, 70% of the students are men and 30% are women; that is, the _____ are men and women are in the _____.
g) Approximately 15% of all students study _____.

**7. Make questions and answers like the example.
The proportions can also be expressed as *ratios*.**

Example: What is the ratio between students of science and students of engineering?
The *ratio between* students of science and students of engineering is 3:2. (three *to* two)

or: The ratio *of* students of science *to* students of engineering is 3:2.

Now write some similar statements about students in your college or university.

8. Look and read:

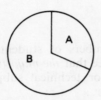

Alloys are mixtures of metals in different proportions. For example, brass is composed of *7 parts of* copper (Cu) *to 3 parts of* zinc (Zn).

Answer these:

a) What are the percentages of copper and zinc in brass?
b) What are A and B in the chart?
c) What is the ratio of copper to zinc?

Now look at the charts and complete the statements:

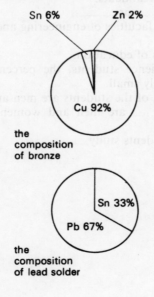

the composition of bronze

the composition of lead solder

d) Bronze is made up of 1 part of _____ to 3 parts of _____ to 46 parts of _____.

e) Expressed as a _____, the composition is: copper _____%, tin _____, zinc _____.

f) The ratio between copper and the other metals is _____.

g) Lead solder consists of _____ of tin to _____ of lead.

h) Lead and tin are in a ratio of_____.

90

Now draw a chart to show the composition of cobalt steel:
35% cobalt (Co), 65% iron (Fe)

Section 3   Direct and inverse proportion

9. Look and read:

There is a *relationship* between the cross-sectional area of a rope and its strength. Its strength is *directly proportional to* its cross-sectional area.

There is also a relationship between the length of these pieces of wood and their strength. Their strength is *inversely proportional to* their length.

Do you think there is a relationship between these? If so, what is it?

> money and happiness
> the growth of a plant and sunlight
> energy and work
> the size of a person's head and his intelligence
> age and beauty

10. Look and read:

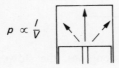

$$p \propto \frac{1}{V}$$

great volume/low pressure   small volume/high pressure

Pressure is inversely proportional to volume; ie *the greater* the volume, *the lower* the pressure. *Conversely*, the smaller the volume, the higher the pressure.

Now complete this:

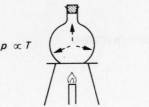

$p \propto T$

low temperature/low pressure   high temperature/high pressure

There is a relationship between the temperature and pressure of gases. Pressure is _____ proportional to temperature; _____ lower the temperature, . . . the pressure. _____, the _____ the temperature, . . . the pressure.

Make a similar statement about volume and temperature:

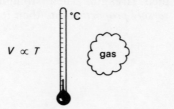

$V \propto T$

low temperature/small volume   high temperature/great volume

11. Look at the diagrams and say whether these statements are true or false. Correct the false statements.

$a \propto F$

a) Acceleration is directly proportional to force.
b) The greater the power of a plane's engines, the slower its acceleration.

92

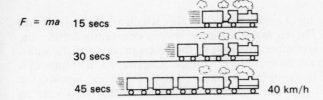

$F = ma$ 15 secs _____

30 secs _____

45 secs _____   40 km/h

True or false?

c) Acceleration is inversely proportional to mass for a given force.
d) The relationship between mass and acceleration is the same kind as that between force and acceleration.
e) The smaller the mass, the faster the acceleration.

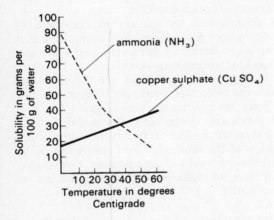

True or false?

f) The solubility of copper sulphate and ammonia is inversely proportional to the temperature of the water.
g) The warmer the water, the greater the solubility of ammonia.
h) The colder the water, the less the solubility of copper sulphate.
i) The relationship between temperature and solubility is not the same for ammonia and copper sulphate.

Section 4   Reading

12. **Read this text and find answers to these questions:**

   a) Why do gases exert pressure on their containers?
   b) Why can gases change their volume, unlike liquids and solids?
   c) What happens when gases are compressed?
   d) What happens when gases are heated?

Pressure

Gases are made up of atoms and molecules, which are in constant and rapid motion. The atoms and molecules are constantly hitting the walls of the gas container. In doing so they exert pressure on the walls.

Gases have no definite shape or volume. The shape and volume of a
5 gas depend on its container. Compared with solids and liquids, the molecules of a gas are relatively far apart. Hence they can be compressed, or forced into a smaller space. But if the volume of a gas is decreased, its pressure increases, because the molecules hit the walls more often and more rapidly. Thus pressure is in inverse proportion
10 to volume.

A liquid, on the other hand, cannot be compressed. If we try to force a liquid into a smaller space, it seeks a way out of the container. The pressure which a liquid exerts on the walls of a container is equal in all directions. This is why liquids are used for transmitting power in
15 different directions, in hydraulic brakes and lifts.

The more a gas is compressed, the greater its resistance to compression. If a large amount of gas is forced into a small space, it becomes difficult to compress further. Under very high pressure, compressed gas can be used for transmitting power.
20 As gas pressure is increased, the molecules are forced closer together. If this continues, the molecules eventually become attached to one another. At this point, the gas changes into a liquid.

The pressure of a gas varies with temperature. Pressure is in direct proportion to absolute temperature, since the higher the temperature,
25 the more rapid the motion of the molecules, and consequently the greater the pressure exerted on the walls of the container. Conversely, the higher the pressure of a gas, the higher its temperature. When a gas is compressed, it becomes hotter.

13. Say whether these relationships are direct or inverse. Then put them in the order in which they occur in the passage.

    a) compression of a gas: resistance to further compression
    b) change in volume: change in pressure
    c) compression of a gas: increase in temperature
    d) distance between molecules: compressibility of substances
    e) change in temperature: change in pressure

14. Discuss the following, using information in the passage:

    a) A car braking system has to be kept full of liquid. If there is a hole in the pipes, the brakes will not work.
    b) Look at the diagram of a refrigerator on page 55. What change of state and temperature occur and why?
    c) A lorry's brakes make use of compressed gas.
    d) Why can tyres filled with air support the weight of a car?
    e) If a water boiler is heated when it is empty, it may explode.
    f) When you pump air into a bicycle tyre, the pump becomes hot.

Unit C   Revision

1. Read the following sentences and fill in the table which follows. The first one has been done for you.

a) When heated, trilead tetroxide produces lead monoxide and oxygen. It changes from an orange-red powder into a yellow solid and a colourless gas.

b) When heated, lead nitrate produces lead monoxide, nitrogen dioxide and oxygen. It is converted from white crystals into a yellow solid, a brown gas and a colourless gas.

c) Heat causes basic copper carbonate to change from a green powder to a black solid, a colourless gas and a colourless liquid. The copper carbonate produces copper oxide, carbon dioxide and water.

d) Heating potassium permanganate produces a change from violet or purple crystals to a blackish or dark-green solid. It releases oxygen and produces potassium manganate and manganese dioxide.

e) If copper sulphate crystals are heated they will change from blue crystals to a white solid and a colourless liquid. Anhydrous copper sulphate and water are produced.

Substance heated	Appearance of substance	Product	Appearance of product
Trilead tetroxide	Orange-red powder	Lead monoxide oxygen	Yellow solid and colourless gas

2. Look at this table:

Abundance of the most common elements by mass					
Crust		Sea water		Whole Earth	
element	%	element	%	element	%
Oxygen	49·4	Oxygen	91	Iron	40–50
Silicon	25·8	Hydrogen	5·7	Oxygen	22–28
Aluminium	7·5	Chlorine	2	Silicon	11–15
Iron	4·7	Sodium	1	Magnesium	9
Calcium	3·4	Magnesium	0·1	Nickel	3–6
Sodium	2·6	Sulphur	0·08	Calcium	1–2
Potassium	2·4	Calcium	0·04	Aluminium	1–2
Magnesium	2	Potassium	0·04		
Hydrogen	0·9	Bromine	0·01		
Titanium	0·5	Carbon	0·003		

Now answer these questions:

a) Which elements constitute approximately 80% of the Earth's crust?

b) What percentage of sea water do oxygen, hydrogen, and chlorine constitute?

c) Express the amounts of oxygen in the Earth's crust, in sea water, and the whole Earth as a ratio.

d) Which element has a ratio 90:20:1 in the whole Earth, in the crust, and in sea water?

e) Which element has an approximate ratio of 5:2 in the crust and in sea water?

f) Which element has a ratio of 85:1 in the crust and sea water?

g) In sea water compare the amount of chlorine with (i) oxygen (ii) bromine.

h) Compare the amount of iron in the whole Earth with the amount of iron in the crust.

3. Look at the table again and read the following passage:

Oxygen, silicon, aluminium and hydrogen together constitute approximately 80% of the Earth's crust, sea and atmosphere. Nitrogen is the main gas in the air, but is not one of the most common elements. Nitrogen forms only a small percentage of the crust and oceans, and the mass of the atmosphere is negligible compared with the total mass of the Earth.

Air is a mixture of gases. Its composition varies and depends to a large extent on plants and animals which control the amounts of oxygen and carbon dioxide by photosynthesis and respiration. Air usually also contains water vapour and dust.

If the dust is removed, the approximate composition by volume is shown in the following table:

Nitrogen	78 %
Oxygen	21 %
Inert gases (mostly argon)	0·93 %
Carbon dioxide	0·03 %

+ small quantities of other gases

Oxygen combines with metals to form oxides. In this way oxygen can be removed from a sample of air and the amount present in the sample can be measured.

Now say whether these statements are true or false. Correct the false statements:

a) Nitrogen is one of the most common elements in the earth.
b) The mass of the atmosphere is small compared with the mass of the crust.
c) The composition of the atmosphere is constant.
d) Air normally contains only gases.
e) The inert gases constitute approximately 1 % of the atmosphere.
f) The inert gases include oxygen.

Unit 10   Measurement 4 Frequency, Tendency, Probability

Section 1   Frequency

1. Look at these diagrams:

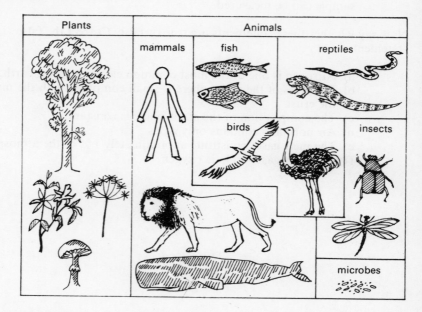

Change the statements on the left, which say how many members of a particular class possess a certain property, into statements of *frequency*, which say *how often* the property occurs:

> *Example:*   All living things consist of cells.   *(always)*
> Living things always consist of cells.

a) Most plants are green.   *(usually)*
b) Many birds live in trees.   *(often/frequently)*
c) Some mammals live in water.   *(sometimes)*
d) A few plants flower at night.   *(occasionally)*
e) Few fish leave the water.   *(rarely)*
f) No living things are two-dimensional.   *(never)*

2. Here are some more properties. Make statements about how often they occur:

> *Examples:*   Plants never swim.
> Animals usually possess tails.
> Reptiles are always cold-blooded.

a) are invisible	k) are three-dimensional
b) breathe	l) are covered with skin
c) have roots	m) are supported by legs
d) lay eggs	n) possess hair
e) suckle young	o) possess lungs
f) eat flesh	p) have wings
g) sing	q) are capable of flying
h) climb trees	r) are able to swim
i) are warm-blooded	s) have the ability to talk
j) are cold-blooded	

Section 2   Tendency

3. Answer these questions:

a) What is the difference between these two generalisations?
   People breathe oxygen.
   People live in houses.
b) Which one says what *always* happens?
c) What does the other one say?
d) Many generalisations are about what usually or *generally* occurs, ie there are *exceptions*, but these are relatively rare. Can you think of any exceptions to the statement that people live in houses?

4. Read this:

Generalisations which have exceptions express a *tendency*. These statements mean the same:
   Most people live in houses.
   People generally live in houses.
   People *tend to* live in houses.

Look at these statements. Add the verb *tend to* to those which express tendency. Add *always* to those which are absolutely true. Add *sometimes, rarely, never* etc. to the others:

a) Plants are green.
b) Humans are two-legged.
c) Birds migrate in groups.
d) Birds live under water.
e) Mammals lay eggs.
f) Insects are smaller than mammals.
g) Fruit is soft.
h) Flowers are blue.

Section 3　Predicting probability

5. Look and read:

		scale
		scale

If something *always* occurs, then it *will certainly* occur.　　100%

If something *nearly always* occurs, then it *will almost*
　　certainly occur.

usually =	*will probably*	
often =	*may well*	
sometimes =	*may/will possibly*	50%
occasionally =	*might*	
rarely⎫		
seldom⎬ =	*probably will not*	
never =	*certainly will not*	0%

The statements about frequency are based on *observation*. From
them we can make *predictions* about the likelihood of something
happening. Thus, we know from observation that *rooms always
have walls*. Therefore we can predict that the next room we see
will certainly have walls.

Make statements about the probability of a room having the following
features:

have ⎰ windows
　　　　at least one chair
　　　　an electric light
　　　　a wooden floor
　　　　wooden walls
　　　　a height of less than 2 metres
　　　　a length of less than 1 metre

be ⎰ cubic in shape
　　　cylindrical in
　　　　shape
　　　surrounded by
　　　　water
　　　joined to other
　　　　rooms
　　　made of glass
　　　bigger than a car

6. Read this:

Some predictions depend on *conditions*.

Example:　*If the room is a laboratory*, then it probably will not
　　　　　　contain beds.

Make similar conditional predictions about the probability of the rooms on
the left having the features on the right.

		a shower
		beds
		a blackboard
a bedroom	contain	a cooker
a laboratory		a microscope
a workshop		an electron microscope
a bathroom	possess	a gas-supply
a hospital ward		a water-supply
a classroom		for sleeping
a kitchen		for learning
	be used	for experiments
		for washing
		for dissecting

7. Read this:

Alternative ways of predicting possibility:

		certain		100%
	(extremely)	{ *probable* }		
	(fairly)	{ *likely* }	that X *will* occur.	
It is		*possible*		50%
	(fairly)	{ *improbable* }		
	(extremely)	{ *unlikely* }		
		certain	that X *will not* occur.	0%

Now observe what percentage of students in your group have the following features:

male	right-handed	a hat
female	shoes	glasses
adult	trousers	blue eyes
child	a dress	brown eyes
animal	long hair	three legs
vegetable	short hair	a moustache
left-handed	a beard	

From these observations make predictions about the next student you meet.

Examples: It is likely that he will be adult.
             If the student is female, it is probable that she will have a dress.

Section 4 Measuring probability

8. Look and read:

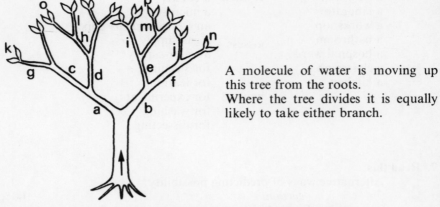

A molecule of water is moving up this tree from the roots.
Where the tree divides it is equally likely to take either branch.

Calculate the chances of the molecule reaching different points.

Examples: The *chances of* the molecule reach*ing* point *a* are *50%* or *one in two*.
The chances of it reaching point *c* are *25%* or *one in four*.

9. Look and read:

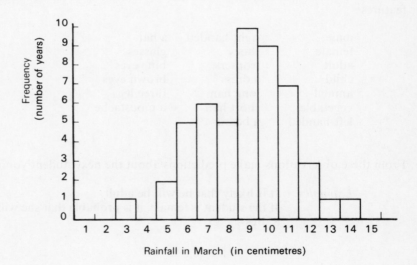

This frequency diagram represents one month's average rainfall in one district over the past 50 years. It shows, for example, that the district had a rainfall of approximately 9 cm 10 times. How often did it have a rainfall of 5 cm?

Now look at these alternative ways of expressing probabilities:

$$\text{There is a/an } \begin{array}{l} \text{(extremely)} \\ \text{(fairly)} \end{array} \left\{\begin{array}{l}\text{strong}\\ \text{high}\end{array}\right\} \qquad \begin{array}{l} \text{(fairly}\\ \text{(extremely)}\end{array} \left\{\begin{array}{l}\text{weak}\\ \text{low}\\ \text{slight}\\ \text{remote}\end{array}\right\} \text{ possibility that X will happen.}$$

There is a/an (extremely)/(fairly) strong/high possibility that X will happen.

(fairly/extremely) weak/low/slight/remote
no

100%
0%

$$\text{The}\left\{\begin{array}{l}\text{possibility}\\ \text{probability}\\ \text{likelihood}\end{array}\right\}\text{that X will happen is}\quad\begin{array}{l}\text{(extremely)}\\ \text{(fairly)}\end{array}\quad\left\{\begin{array}{l}\text{high.}\\ \text{strong.}\end{array}\right\}$$

$$\left\{\begin{array}{l}\text{low.}\\ \text{weak.}\\ \text{slight.}\\ \text{remote.}\end{array}\right\}$$
nil.

100%
0%

Make predictions like these, from the frequency diagram, about the possibility of

a rainfall of 8 cm.
                10 cm.
                 6 cm.
                 4 cm.
                12 cm.
              more than 20 cm.
              less than 1 cm.
              more than 14 cm.
              between 6 and 10 cm.
              between 11 and 15 cm.

Example: The possibility that the district will have a rainfall of less than 1 cm is extremely low.

10. Look and read:

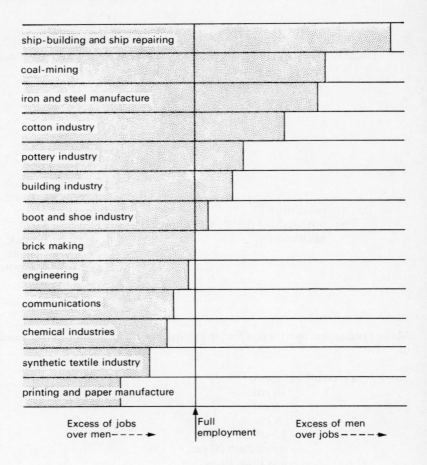

The above diagram represents the proportion of jobs to men in various industries. In ship-building, for example, there are many more workers than jobs, so there is serious unemployment.

Give the name of:

　　　a) an industry which has too many workers, or not enough jobs;
　　　b) an industry which has too few workers;
　　　c) an industry where the ratio of men to jobs is exactly one to one.

Unemployment is increasing. What are the relative possibilities of workers in different industries keeping or losing their jobs?

　　　d) If a man works in the chemical industries, is it probable that he will lose his job?
　　　e) In which industry is a man least likely to lose his job?

f) What possibility is there that a building worker will keep his job?

g) Is there much likelihood that a man in communications will lose his job? (much, some or little)

Now make five more predictions, using sentences like those in exercise 9.

11. Look and read:

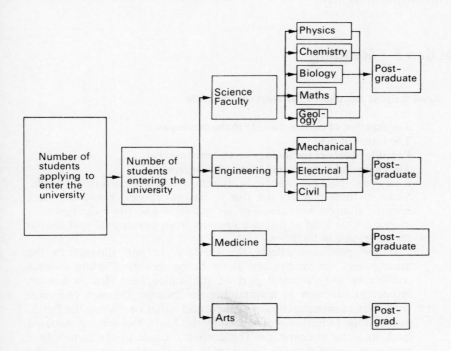

This chart shows the proportions of students entering a university and studying different subjects.

Complete these sentences:

a) (revision) The areas of the rectangles are . . . to the numbers of students.

b) The next student of engineering you meet will _____ be an electrical or mechanical engineer.

c) The _____ of a student entering the university are about one in _____.

d) If a student enters the university he is more likely to study _____ than _____.

e) A student of _____ may well continue to do postgraduate studies.

f) _____ that he is accepted for the university, every student has some _____ of becoming a postgraduate.

g) A student of biology . . . be in the science faculty.

h) An engineer . . . be in the arts faculty.
i) A student of _____ might become a postgraduate.
j) It is less probable that a scientist will study _____ than _____ .
k) It is possible that . . .
l) There is a strong possibility that . . .
m) The probability that . . . is slight.
n) A student of science may . . .
o) Alternatively, he may . . .

Section 5   Reading

12. Read the text and choose the most suitable title:

The function of carbon dioxide in the atmosphere
The future of man
Possible effects of technology on the environment
The control of temperature in the environment

Every year there are changes in climate in different parts of the world. Some of these changes are due to natural causes. However, some climatic changes are caused by air pollution and these changes may increase. One kind of pollution results from burning oil and coal in
5 transport and in factories.

If the pollution affects the level of carbon dioxide in the atmosphere, the results are likely to be serious. Carbon dioxide constitutes only a small part of the atmosphere. But it has an important function in maintaining the balance between radiation
10 from the sun entering the atmosphere and radiation leaving the Earth. Some of the radiation is absorbed by the Earth and some is radiated back into the atmosphere. The carbon dioxide in the atmosphere prevents some of the radiation from leaving the atmosphere. Thus the heat remains in the atmosphere and carbon dioxide helps to prevent
15 the temperature of the Earth from falling.

If the proportion of carbon dioxide in the atmosphere is increased as a result of air pollution, the temperature of the atmosphere may rise. This might eventually cause the ice in the north and the south poles to melt. If this happened, the sea level would rise and parts of the
20 Earth would be flooded. The likelihood of this happening is remote, but the possibility exists.

There is also a fairly strong possibility that the dust level in the atmosphere will rise as a result of industrial pollution. This dust pollution will reflect sunlight back into space. If this happens, less
25 sunlight will reach the Earth and the temperature will fall.

Another danger comes from the destruction of the Earth's vegetation, such as the forests of Brazil, which are being cleared to make way for farmland and cities. Trees use carbon dioxide and their destruction may upset the balance of carbon dioxide in the
30 atmosphere.

Look at these notes on possible future events and their effects. Using information from the passage, discuss whether they are certain, probable, possible or unlikely. Then put them in the order in which they occur in the passage.

a) temperature of atmosphere↑ ⟶ polar ice↓
b) new cities and farmland ⟶ destruction of vegetation
c) air pollution↑ ⟶ level of CO_2 in atmosphere↑
d) air pollution ⟶ climatic changes
e) destruction of vegetation ⟶ balance of CO_2 upset
f) industrial pollution↑ ⟶ dust in atmosphere↑
g) CO_2↑ ⟶ level of radiation↑
h) polar ice↓ ⟶ sea level↑
i) burning oil and coal ⟶ air pollution↑
j) dust in atmosphere↑ ⟶ sunlight reflected back
k) sunlight reflected back ⟶ earth's temperature↓
l) level of radiation↑ ⟶ temperature of atmosphere↑
m) sea level↑ ⟶ parts of earth flooded

Unit 11　Process 4　Method

Section 1　How things should be done

1. Look and read:

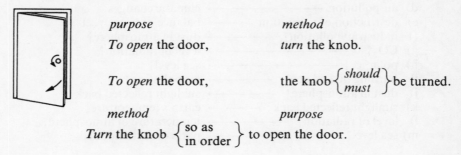

purpose	*method*
To open the door,	*turn* the knob.

To open the door,　　　　the knob $\left\{\begin{array}{l} should \\ must \end{array}\right\}$ be turned.

method	*purpose*

Turn the knob $\left\{\begin{array}{l} \text{so as} \\ \text{in order} \end{array}\right\}$ to open the door.

Now look at this radio. What must be done to operate it?

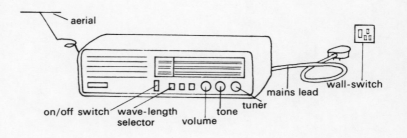

aerial

on/off switch　wave-length
　　　　　　　selector
　　　　　　　　　volume
　　　　　　　　tone
　　　　　　　tuner
mains lead　　wall-switch

From the table below, make four sentences like each of the examples above.

purpose	*method*
switch on the set	press the on/off switch
adjust the volume	turn the volume knob
adjust the tone	turn the tone knob
select the right wave-length	press the wave-length selector
find the required radio station	turn the tuner
obtain better reception	fit an aerial
switch on the mains	press the wall-switch down
connect the radio with the mains	plug in the mains lead
operate the radio	

2. Look at these diagrams and instructions for operating a camera:

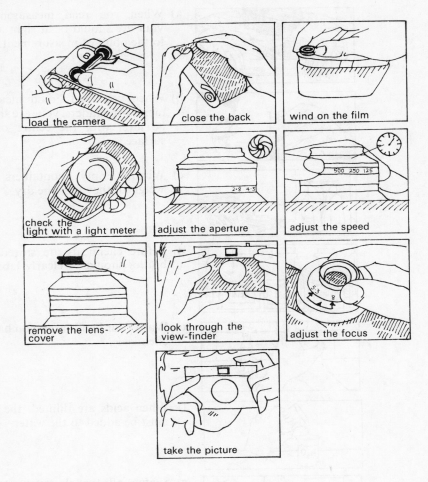

load the camera

close the back

wind on the film

check the light with a light meter

adjust the aperture

adjust the speed

remove the lens-cover

look through the view-finder

adjust the focus

take the picture

Now write ten instructions like these examples:

> *After loading* the camera, the film *should be wound on*. The camera *must be loaded before taking* the picture. *While adjusting* the focus, *look* through the view-finder.

3. Look at these examples:

Before switching on the radio, $\left\{ \begin{array}{l} \textit{make sure} \\ \textit{ensure} \end{array} \right\}$ that the mains lead is plugged in.

Make sure that the camera is loaded before taking the picture.

Rewrite the following precautions like the examples:

a) When you read measurements, your eye should be at right angles to the point of measurement.

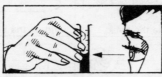

b) When you read liquid measurements in cylinders, your eye should be level with the centre of the surface.

c) When empty containers are weighed, they must be dry.

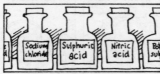

d) Before chemicals are stored, the bottles should be clearly labelled.

e) Wash your hands after you handle chemicals.

f) When acids are diluted, the acid must be added to the water.

g) Switch off the electricity before you change light bulbs.

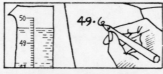

h) When you observe the results of experiments, record the results accurately.

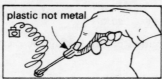

i) When electrical parts are unscrewed, the screwdriver must be insulated.

Section 2　How things may be done

4. Look again at the radio on page 108 and at these examples:

method   *purpose*

How $\left\{\begin{array}{c} may \\ can \end{array}\right\}$ the radio *be switched on*?

purpose   *method*

The radio $\left\{\begin{array}{c} may \\ can \end{array}\right\}$ *be switched on* by pressing the on/off switch.

Make other questions and answers like these.

5. Look at these instruments and tools and then make sentences describing what can be done with them:

Example: Temperature $\left\{\begin{array}{c} can \\ may \end{array}\right\}$ be measured $\left\{\begin{array}{l} by\ means\ of \\ by\ using \\ with \end{array}\right\}$ a thermometer.

purpose	*instrument or tool*
for measuring temperature	a thermometer
for viewing small objects	a microscope
for viewing distant objects	a telescope
for pouring liquids	a funnel
for heating chemicals	a bunsen burner
for weighing substances	a balance
for hammering nails	a hammer
for turning nuts & bolts	a spanner
for turning screws	a screwdriver
for measuring pressure	a barometer
for lifting things	pulleys
for testing acids and alkalis	litmus paper

111

6. Read this:

Alternative ways of making a magnet

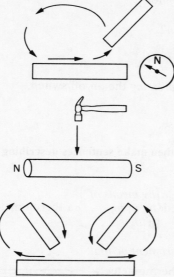

Method 1: stroke a piece of iron with a magnet. Always stroke it in the same direction. Test the new magnet with a compass.

Method 2: place a bar of iron in a north-south direction. Hit it with a hammer. Test with a compass.

Method 3: stroke a piece of iron with two magnets. Take care to use two different poles and stroke in opposite directions. Test with a compass.

Now complete these descriptions:

      Method 1: A magnet may be made by . . .
      The iron should always be . . .
      The magnet can be . . .

      Method 2: Alternatively, a bar of iron . . .
      and . . . . The magnet . . .

      Method 3: Another method of making a magnet is by . . .
      Two different poles must . . .
      and the bar must . . .

Now write descriptions with the aid of these words and diagrams:

      Alternative ways of demagnetising a magnet

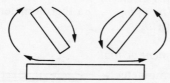

Method 1: A magnet may be demagnetised . . .
                 placing . . . E⟮   ⟯W hitting . . .

Method 2: Alternatively, . . . drop . . . several times . . .

Method 3: Another method of . . . heat . . .   bunsen burner.

112

7. Look at these diagrams:

Different ways of separating materials

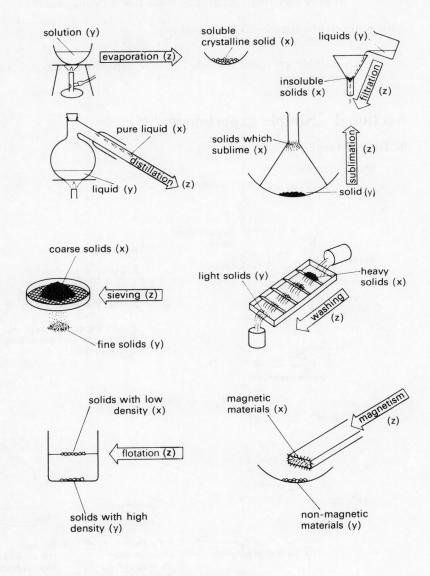

Note: x = the material to be separated
y = the other material
z = the method of separating them

Now make sequences of sentences like this example:

> One method of separating materials is by filtration.
> Alternatively, materials may be separated by sieving.
> Another method of separating materials is by magnetism.

Now write eight sentences like this example:

> A soluble crystalline solid $\left\{ \begin{matrix} can \\ may \end{matrix} \right\}$ be separated from a solution evaporation.

Section 3   Simple experiments

8. Look and read:

Making crystals:

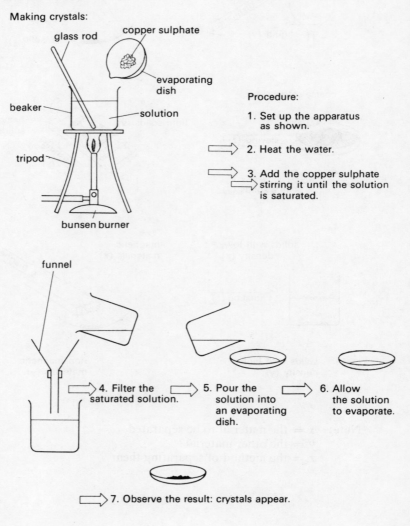

Procedure:

1. Set up the apparatus as shown.

2. Heat the water.

3. Add the copper sulphate stirring it until the solution is saturated.

4. Filter the saturated solution.

5. Pour the solution into an evaporating dish.

6. Allow the solution to evaporate.

7. Observe the result: crystals appear.

Now complete this description of the experiment:

The *purpose* of the experiment is to make _____.
The *apparatus* consists of . . .
The *substance* to be crystallised is _____.
The *method* of carrying out the experiment is by _____.
The *procedure* is as follows:
First, the apparatus is set up _____.
Then, the water is _____.
Meanwhile, the copper sulphate _____ and stirred until . . . .
_____, the saturated solution _____.
Next, the solution . . . .
_____, the solution . . . .
Finally, the result is observed.
The *result* is that crystals appear.

9. Look and read:

Separation of gunpowder:

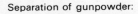

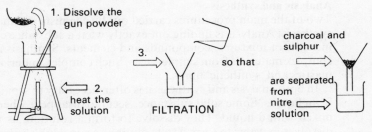

1. Dissolve the gun powder

2. heat the solution

3.

so that

FILTRATION

charcoal and sulphur

are separated from nitre solution

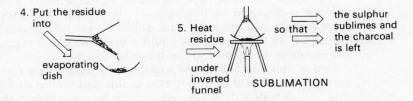

4. Put the residue into

evaporating dish

5. Heat residue

so that

under inverted funnel

SUBLIMATION

the sulphur sublimes and the charcoal is left

6. Meanwhile,

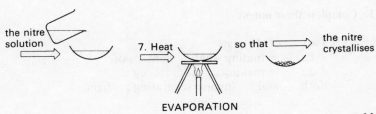

the nitre solution

7. Heat

so that

the nitre crystallises

EVAPORATION

115

Now complete this description:

> The purpose . . . .
> The apparatus . . . .
> The substance . . . .
> The method . . . .
> The procedure . . . .
> The result . . . .

Section 4   Reading

10. Read this text and find answers to these questions:

> a) What methods of separating materials are discussed?
> b) What are: a solution?
>   a solvent?
>   a solute?
>   a filtrate?

Analysis and synthesis

Two of the main procedures carried out by chemists are analysis and synthesis. Analysis is finding out exactly what a substance consists of in terms of mixtures, compounds and elements. Synthesis is making complex materials from simpler ones. Such complex materials include
5 plastics and 'synthetic' fibres.

In both analysis and synthesis it is often necessary to separate solids from liquids. Some solid substances seem to disappear when they are mixed with a liquid. They dissolve to form a solution, as when salt dissolves in water to form a salt solution. An insoluble substance can
10 be separated from a soluble one by filtration. The insoluble substance remains on the filter while the liquid, or filtrate, passes through.

A dissolved substance, or solute, can be separated from the liquid in which it is dissolved by boiling away the solvent. This process is evaporation. Alternatively, the solvent can be separated by
15 distillation. In this process the liquid is boiled so that it evaporates. The vapour is then cooled so that it condenses again.

Two or more liquids mixed together can separate by fractional distillation, provided that they boil at different temperatures. The liquid which boils at the lowest temperature is separated first, then the
20 one with the next lowest boiling point, and so on. This process is used for separating petrol, paraffin and engine oil from crude oil in refineries.

11. Complete these notes:

> Two . . . of chemists:
> 1. . . . = finding what . . . consists of.
> 2. . . . = making . . . from . . . , eg . . .
> Both . . . and . . . involve separating . . . from . . .

116

Methods of separating:
1. Aim: separating ... from ... in solution.
   Method: ...
2. Aim: separating ... from ...
   Method 1: ... = ...
   Method 2: ...   (Procedure: ...)
3. Aim: separating solutes with ...
   Method: ...   (Procedure: ...)

Unit 12   Consolidation

Section 1   Revision and reading practice

1. Look at this diagram and then read the passage below:

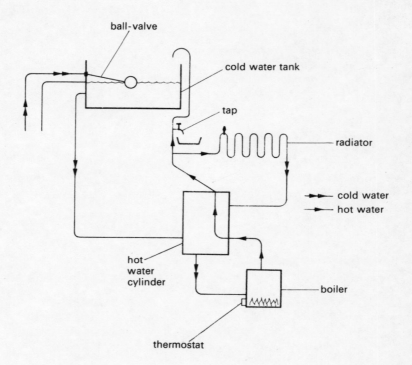

(A) A hot water system consists of a boiler and tanks for storing water. Other parts include taps and a thermostat, which is fitted on the boiler. (B) The system may also include radiators. (C) The boiler is situated at the bottom of the system. (D) It serves to heat the water. (E) Heating the water causes it (F) to rise. (G) When the hot water tap is turned on, water comes from the top of the hot water cylinder. Simultaneously, cold water flows into the cylinder from the cold water tank.

(H) The flow of water into the cold water tank is controlled by means of a ball valve. (I) The valve is connected by a bar to (J) a ball-shaped metal float. This floats because (K) it is hollow. As the tank is filled with water, the ball rises and the valve closes.

The cold water tank is situated above the hot water cylinder. Cold water flows out of the tank as a result of gravity.

The function of the thermostat is to control the temperature of the water. This ensures that the water is (L) warm enough, but prevents it from becoming (M) too hot. (N) The water has a temperature of approximately 60°C. A tank with a capacity of 60 litres is generally sufficient for an average family.

A radiator is usually rectangular in cross-section, with wide, flat sides. (O) This shape gives it a large surface area in proportion to its volume. Consequently, it gives out more heat.

The above description includes expressions which have been in previous units. The letters show their positions. Match the letters with the following:

Example: (A) is a description of structure.

a) Another description of structure.
b) A sequence of actions.
c) A statement of possibility.
d) A sufficient quantity.
e) A cause.
f) A result.
g) A simple measurement.
h) A relative measurement.
i) An excessive quantity.
j) A location.
k) A description of method.
l) A statement of function.
m) A shape.
n) Another property.

2. Now answer these questions:

a) Where is the hot water cylinder situated in relation to the cold water tank?
b) Why is part of the valve described as 'ball-shaped'?
c) Describe some of the other properties of the ball-float.
d) What causes the water to flow out of the cold water tank?
e) What is the function of the boiler?
f) What does the ball-valve consist of?
g) How much water does a hot water cylinder usually contain? (approximately)
h) What may happen if the water becomes too hot?
i) What happens as the ball-float rises to the top of the tank?
j) What is the result of heating the water?
k) How can hot water be drawn from the top of the cylinder?
l) Why does a radiator give out a large quantity of heat?
m) Why does the hot water cylinder give out less heat?

3. Read this:

What happens during an earthquake?
During an earthquake, the surface of the Earth moves. The shock is produced by waves which travel through the rock. These waves are usually the result of the movement of large masses of rock below

the surface of the Earth. Many earthquakes begin under the sea. These cause very big waves in the sea.

Now complete this:

Earthquakes are movements in the Earth's _____. _____ earthquakes, rocks move, thereby . . . . The waves travel to the surface and bring about the _____. Big waves in the sea result from . . . . During the earthquake, first _____ move, then . . ., and finally . . . .

Now read this:

Earthquakes may take place anywhere on the Earth's surface. However, they are most likely to occur in certain regions. These are shown on the map below. Earthquake regions are usually near mountains or volcanoes. Outside these areas, earthquakes are generally weak.

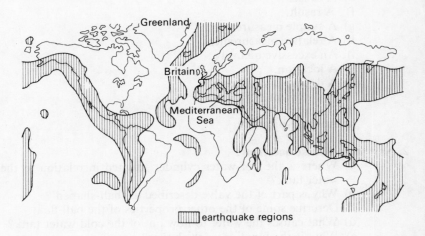

earthquake regions

Say whether these statements are true or false. Correct the false statements.

a) Earthquakes tend to occur under the sea.
b) Earthquakes rarely take place in the north of Russia.
c) It is possible that an earthquake will take place in the north of Russia next year.
d) The chances of an earthquake occurring next month are greater in the west of South America than in the east of South America.
e) The Mediterranean Sea is surrounded by earthquake regions.
f) Earthquakes never happen in Greenland.
g) Countries where earthquakes are likely to occur include Britain.
h) In the majority of African countries there is only a slight possibility that an earthquake will occur next month.
i) The possibility of an earthquake occurring in one region may be observed by predicting the frequency of earthquakes in that region.

120

4. Now read this:

The measurement of earthquakes

During an earthquake the pressure waves may travel at a maximum speed of 650 km/s. The duration of earthquakes varies: an earthquake may have a duration of a second or it may continue intermittently for days. The force of an earthquake can be measured by means of special instruments. There is also a scale of measurement based on the effects of earthquakes. This scale ranges from earthquakes which are too weak to be observed by man to those which are capable of destroying everything made by man.

Answer these questions:

a) Name four things about earthquakes which can be measured.
b) On the scale of earthquake measurement, what is the strength of an earthquake proportional to?
c) Why can we not observe some earthquakes?
d) What is the effect of extremely bad earthquakes?
e) The study of earthquakes is called 'seismology'. What is a seismometer?

5. Finally, read this:

Some of the bad effects of earthquakes in towns can be prevented by making special buildings. These have two kinds of structure. In one kind of building the parts are made of light, flexible materials. The parts are woven together, like a basket. This structure and the properties of the materials enable the building to move without breaking. The other kind of building is like a box in structure. It is made of heavy, rigid materials. The lower part of the building must have a much greater mass than the upper part.

Now complete these:

This is a basket. It is strong because . . . . and because . . . .

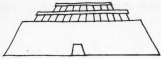

This building is strong because . . . and because . . . .

This building is not good for earth-quake regions because the roof is . . . .

Section 2   Appearance, fact and proof

6. Look and read:

Is this picture two-dimensional or three-dimensional?

It *appears to be* three-dimensional, but *in fact* it is two-dimensional.

Now complete these:

a)

This . . . a hemisphere, . . . consists of curved and straight lines.

b)

A spoon in a glass of water . . . broken, . . . not broken.

c)

These lines *converge*.

These lines are ———.

If you look along a road, the sides of the road appear to ———, but in fact . . . .

122

d)

_____ the Sun approaches the horizon, its diameter _____ become bigger. The farther it is from the _____, the smaller it appears. The nearer it is to the horizon, ... Its diameter appears to be ... to its distance from the horizon.

_____, the size of the Sun does not vary; it is _____. The *apparent* change in size is caused by dust in the air near the horizon.

e)

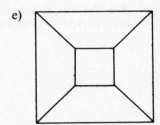

Look at this figure. It appears to be _____-dimensional, but in fact .... . The small square sometimes appears to be behind the big square. Sometimes it appears to be _____ the big square. In fact it is _____ the big square.

7. Now look at these figures and answer the questions, saying what they appear to be and what they are in fact:

a)

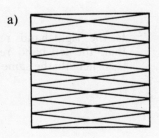

Is this a rectangle or a square?

b)

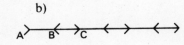

Have lines AB and BC the same length or different lengths?

123

c)

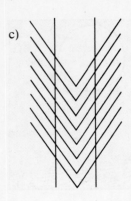

Do the vertical lines converge or are they parallel?

d)

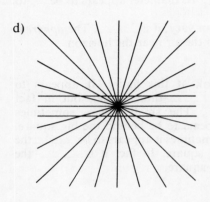

Are the top and bottom horizontal lines curved or straight?

e)

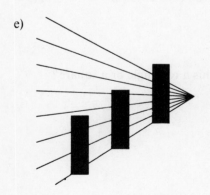

Is the right-hand rectangle higher than the left-hand rectangle or are their heights the same?

8. Now read these sentences:

> We *can prove that* figure (a) is a square by measuring the sides. *To show that* the vertical lines in figure (c) are parallel, a ruler should be placed along them.

Complete these:

>   a) We can _____ that lines AB and BC in figure (b) have the same length by . . . .
>   b) . . . the horizontal lines in figure (d) are in fact straight, ...
>   c) To prove that the heights of the rectangles in figure (e) . . . , they . . . .
>   d) By placing a ruler along the vertical lines in figure (c), we can . . . .

Section 3   More simple experiments

9. Read these instructions:

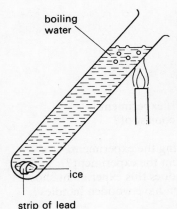

boiling water

ice

strip of lead

Purpose:
To show that water is a bad conductor of heat.

Procedure:
Wrap a strip of lead round a piece of ice. Drop the ice into a test-tube which contains water.

ice

lead

Heat the water at the top of the test-tube until it boils.

Observation: When the water boils, the ice does not melt.
Conclusion: Water is a bad conductor of heat.

Now complete this:

>   a) By doing this experiment, we can prove that . . . .
>   b) The apparatus for this experiment consists of . . . .
>   c) After the ice is dropped into the test-tube . . . .
>   d) The ice sinks to the bottom of the test-tube because . . . .
>   e) During this experiment, we observe that . . . .
>   f) The conclusion drawn from this experiment is that . . . .

125

10. Now read this description:

Different materials conduct heat at different speeds. This can be shown by doing a simple experiment. Some rods are covered with wax and attached to a metal tank. The rods have the same size but are made of different materials. The tank is filled with hot water.

The wax on the rods soon starts to melt. On the copper rod, a large amount of wax melts. Hardly any wax melts on the wooden rod. On the other rods, the amount of melted wax varies. This shows that some materials are good conductors of heat, while others are bad conductors of heat.

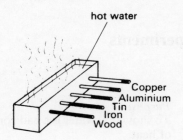

Answer these questions:

    a) What is the purpose of this experiment?
    b) What does the apparatus consist of?
    c) What is the procedure?
    d) What can we observe during the experiment?
    e) What can we conclude from the experiment?
    f) What property of copper does this experiment show?
    g) Why do cooking pots often have wooden handles?

11. Look at this diagram:

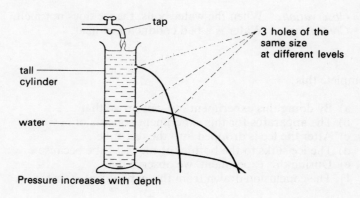

Now complete these sentences:

Purpose: To show that . . .

Apparatus: This consists of . . .

Procedure: Place the cylinder . . .
                 Turn on the tap so that . . .

Observation: The water comes most quickly . . . and most slowly . . .

Conclusion: Pressure is higher at . . . than near . . . of the water.
                 Therefore, pressure increases . . . ie pressure is
                 proportional . . .

Glossary

This list gives the pronunciations of the technical and less common words used in this book and definitions of those words that are not fully explained in the text or diagrams. An asterisk (*) means that a word in the definition is itself explained in the Glossary. The number after each entry indicates the unit in which the word first appears. The letters RT stand for 'Reading Text', and the number given after this again indicates the unit number of the reading text in which the word first occurs.

Pronunciations are shown in the system that is used in the Longman *Dictionary of Contemporary English*. The symbols are shown in this table, with a key word for each. The letters printed in **bold type** represent the sound value of the symbol.

Consonants

p	pea		f	few		ʃ	fishing		h	hot
b	bay		v	view		ʒ	pleasure		m	sum
t	tea		θ	thing		tʃ	choose		n	sun
d	day		ð	then		dʒ	jump		ŋ	sung
k	key		s	soon		l	led		j	yet
g	gay		z	zoo		r	red		w	wet

Vowels

iː	sheep		ɔː	caught		eɪ	make		ɪə	here
ɪ	ship		ʊ	put		əʊ	note		eə	there
e	bed		uː	boot		aɪ	bite		ʊə	poor
æ	bad		ʌ	cut		aʊ	now		eɪə	player
ɑː	calm		ɜː	bird		ɔɪ	boy		əʊə	lower
ɒ	cot		ə	about					aɪə	tire
									aʊə	tower
									ɔɪə	employer

Notes

1. A small raised /ʳ/ at the end of a word means that the /r/ is pronounced if a vowel follows (at the beginning of the text word), but not otherwise. For example, *far* /fɑːʳ/ means that *far away* is pronounced /fɑːr əweɪ/ but *far down* is /fɑː daʊn/.

2. The italic /ə/ means that the sound /ə/ can be used but is often omitted. It may be found before the consonants /m, n, ŋ, l, r/ in certain positions. For example, *travel* /ˈtrævəl/ means that the pronounciation /ˈtrævəl/ is possible but /ˈtrævl/ may be more common.

3. The mark /ˈ/ means that the following syllable has *main stress*, and /ˌ/ means that the following syllable has *secondary stress*. For example, *understand* /ˌʌndəˈstænd/.

ability /ə'bɪlətɪ/ being able to do something 5

absorbent /əb'zɔːbənt/ able to take in liquid 3

absorption /əb'zɔːpʃən/ 6

accelerator /ək'seləreɪtə^r/ 5

accuracy /'ækjərəsɪ/ exactness, correctness RT 4

Aconcagua /ˌækɒŋ'kɑːgwə/ 4

adequate /'ædɪkwət/ enough 7

adjacent /ə'dʒeɪsənt/ 2

adjust /ə'dʒʌst/ make a thing right 5

adrenal /ə'driːnəl/ gland of the body which produces a substance* (adrenalin) needed when a person is angry or afraid RT 5

aerial /'eərɪəl/ 1

alcohol /'ælkəhɒl/ 4

alkali /'ælkəlaɪ/ 8

alloy /'ælɔɪ/ 9

aluminium /ˌæljʊ'mɪnɪəm/ 7

Amazon /'æməzən/ 4

ammonia /ə'məʊnɪə/ 9

amoeba /ə'miːbə/ 4

ampere /'æmpeə^r/ 4

anaemia /ə'niːmɪə/ 7

analysis /ə'næləsɪs/ RT 11

aneroid barometer /ˌænərɔɪd bə'rɒmɪtə^r/ barometer worked by a vacuum box with springy walls B

angle /'æŋgəl/ RT 2

angular /'æŋgjʊlə^r/ measured as an angle RT 2

anhydrous /æn'haɪdrəs/ without water C

aorta /eɪ'ɔːtə/ 6

apparatus /ˌæpə'reɪtəs/ 1

appearance /ə'pɪərəns/ way something looks 12

approximately /ə'prɒksɪmətlɪ/ 4

April /'eɪprəl/ 4

area /'eərɪə/ 1

argon /'ɑːgɒn/ (A) 7

atmosphere /'ætməsfɪə^r/ 3

atmospheric /ˌætməs'ferɪk/ 5

attract /ə'trækt/ pull towards 8

August /'ɔːgəst/ 4

auricle /'ɔːrɪkəl/ 8

average /'ævərɪdʒ/ 4

axle /'æksəl/ 3

bacteria /bæk'tɪərɪə/ 4

balance /'bæləns/ keeping two things equal, so that one does not become greater than the other RT 10

balloon /bə'luːn/ bag filled with gas lighter than air 8

barometer /bə'rɒmɪtə^r/ 5

beri-beri /ˌberɪ'berɪ/ RT 7

bimetallic /ˌbaɪmə'tælɪk/ consisting of two different metals RT 8

bromine /'brəʊmiːn/ (Br) C

bunsen burner /ˌbʌnsən 'bɜːnə^r/ 2

burette /bjʊə'ret/ 7

bury /'berɪ/ put under the ground RT 6

cadmium /'kædmɪəm/ (Cd) 2

calcium /'kælsɪəm/ (Ca) 7

capacity /kə'pæsətɪ/ (1) amount a container can hold 4; (2) being able to do something 5

carbohydrate /ˌkɑːbəʊ'haɪdreɪt/ RT 6

carbon /'kɑːbən/ (C) RT 6

carbonic /kɑː'bɒnɪk/ 8

cartilage /'kɑːtəlɪdʒ/ substance* found instead of bone in young animals, and around the joints of older animals RT 5

casing /'keɪsɪŋ/ outer covering 3

centi- /'sentɪ/ hundredth 4

charcoal /'tʃɑːkəʊl/ black fuel made by burning wood slowly with little air 8

chemical /'kemɪkəl/ RT 1

chloride /'klɔːraɪd/ 7

chlorine /'klɔːriːn/ (Cl) RT 1

chlorophyll /'klɒrəfɪl/ 8

chromium /'krəʊmɪəm/ (Cr) 2

circuit /'sɜːkɪt/ the complete path of an electric current RT 8

circular /'sɜːkjələ^r/ 1

circulatory /'sɜːkjʊlətərɪ/ RT 5

circumference /sə'kʌmfərəns/ 4

climate /'klaɪmɪt/ the average weather conditions of a place RT 10

climatic /klaɪ'mætɪk/ belonging to the climate* of a place RT 10

cobalt /'kəʊbɔːlt/ (Co) 2

coefficient of expansion /kəʊɪˌfɪʃənt əv ɪk'spænʃən/ the number which shows the amount by which a substance* expands* for a given change in temperature RT 8

column /'kɒləm/ 2

combine /kəm'baɪn/ join together chemically RT 1

combustible /kəm'bʌstəbl/ 1

combustion /kəm'bʌstʃən/ 8

compare /kəm'peə^r/ look at things to see how they are the same or different 9

compass /'kʌmpəs/ 11

compound /'kɒmpaʊnd/ substance* formed by uniting different elements* RT 1

compress /kəm'pres/ press together into a

smaller space 6

concave /ˌkɒnˈkeɪv/ 2

concentric /kənˈsentrɪk/ having the same centre RT 3

conclude /kənˈkluːd/ decide as a result of reasoning 12

conical /ˈkɒnɪkəl/ 1

consequence /ˈkɒnsɪkwəns/ RT 8

considerable /kənˈsɪdərəbəl/ 7

constant /ˈkɒnstənt/ unchanging 4

constitute /ˈkɒnstɪtjuːt/ make up C

consume /kənˈsjuːm/ eat, use up 7

contact /ˈkɒntækt/ point where an electrical circuit is completed by one metal part touching another RT 8

make contact /meɪk ˈkɒntækt/ to touch RT 8

contents (of the earth) /ˈkɒntents (əv ðɪ ˌɜːθ)/ the parts or substances* which the earth contains RT 3

contract /kənˈtrækt/ RT 8

contraction /kənˈtrækʃən/ the action of contracting (becoming smaller) RT 8

converge /kənˈvɜːdʒ/ come together at one point RT 2

conversely /kənˈvɜːslɪ/ 9

convert /kənˈvɜːt/ change 8

crystal /ˈkrɪstl/ 7

crystalline /ˈkrɪstəlaɪn/ having a regular arrangement of atoms 11

crystallise /ˈkrɪstəlaɪz/ form crystals 8

cubic /ˈkjuːbɪk/ 1

cycle /ˈsaɪkəl/ repeating set of events 6

cylinder /ˈsɪlɪndəʳ/ 1

cylindrical /sɪˈlɪndrɪkəl/ 1

cytoplasm /ˈsaɪtəʊplæzəm/ 3

decay /dɪˈkeɪ/ decompose* and rot as a result of bacterial action 6

December /dɪˈsembəʳ/ 4

deci- /ˈdesɪ/ tenth 4

decompose /ˌdiːkəmˈpəʊz/ break down into simpler substances* 6

decomposition /ˌdiːkɒmpəˈzɪʃən/ RT 6

decrease /dɪˈkriːs/ become smaller, make smaller 8

deficiency /dɪˈfɪʃənsɪ/ not enough, insufficient quantity RT 7

deformed /dɪˈfɔːmd/ changed from normal shape RT 7

degree /dɪˈgriː/ a unit in the measurement of angles (eg 42°) RT 2; a unit in the measurement of temperature (eg 27°C) 4

density /ˈdensətɪ/ 4

depend on /dɪˈpend ˌɒn/ be controlled and influenced by 8

desert /ˈdezət/ 2

device /dɪˈvaɪs/ instrument* 5

diagonal /daɪˈægənəl/ 1

diameter /daɪˈæmɪtəʳ/ a straight line through the centre of a circle or square, going from one side to the other RT 3

diamond /ˈdaɪəmənd/ very hard brilliant precious stone 1

diet /ˈdaɪət/ the kind of food and drink which a person usually takes RT 7

digest /daɪˈdʒest, dɪˈdʒest/ change food into a form which the body can use 4

digestion /daɪˈdʒestʃən, dɪˈdʒestʃən/ the action or process of digesting* food RT 5

digestive /daɪˈdʒestɪv, dɪˈdʒestɪv/ RT 5

dilute /daɪˈluːt, daɪˈljuːt/ make weaker or thinner 11

dimension /daɪˈmenʃən/ measurement, eg length, width, height 1

dimensional /daɪˈmenʃənəl/ 1

disintegrate /dɪsˈɪntəgreɪt/ break into small pieces 8

dissect /dɪˈsekt/ cut up in order to examine 10

dissolve /dɪˈzɒlv/ RT 1

distil /dɪˈstɪl/ make a liquid into a vapour, then make the vapour into liquid 5

distributed /dɪˈstrɪbjuːtɪd/ found in different places 2

drains /dreɪnz/ pipes or channels to carry away waste 6

duration /djʊˈreɪʃən, dʒʊˈreɪʃən/ time during which something lasts or exists 4

dynamo /ˈdaɪnəməʊ/ 5

effect /ɪˈfekt/ result of a cause 8

eg /ˌiːˈdʒiː/ = for example 1

eject /ɪˈdʒekt/ put out RT 5

electrolyte /ɪˈlektrəlaɪt/ 3

element /ˈelɪmənt/ substance* which cannot be split up into simpler substances* RT 1

emerge /ɪˈmɜːdʒ/ come out 6

endocrine /ˈendəʊkrɪn, ˈendəʊkraɪn/ RT 5

engineering /ˌendʒɪˈnɪərɪŋ/ 9

environment /ɪnˈvaɪərənmənt/ the surroundings and conditions in which people live RT 10

epithelial /epɪˈθiːlɪəl/ RT 5

Equator /ɪˈkweɪtəʳ/ an imaginary* line round the world, halfway between its top and bottom points RT 2

essential /ɪˈsenʃəl/ absolutely necessary RT 7

etiolated /'i:tɪəleɪtɪd/ (of plants) pale owing to lack of light 8

evaporate /ɪ'væpəreɪt/ 6

evaporation /ɪ,væpə'reɪʃən/ 6

exactly /ɪg'zæktlɪ/ 4

except /ɪk'sept/ but not including 1

exception /ɪk'sepʃən/ something not covered by a rule 10

excess /ɪk'ses/ 7

excessive /ɪk'sesɪv/ 7

exert pressure /ɪg'zз:t ,preʃəʳ/ put pressure on something RT 9

expand /ɪk'spænd/ become larger RT 8

expansion /ɪk'spænʃən/ the action of expanding* (growing larger) RT 8

explode /ɪk'spləʊd/ burst, break up violently* RT 9

exposed /ɪk'spəʊzd/ laid open 8

exterior /ɪk'stɪərɪə/ 2

external /ɪk'stз:nəl/ of the outside 5

extinguish /ɪk'stɪŋgwɪʃ/ 6

extremes /ɪk'stri:mz/ highest and lowest points 4

fact /fækt/ real truth 12

February /'februərɪ/ 4

fertile /'fз:taɪl/ (of land) producing many crops 7

fertilise /'fз:tɪlaɪz/ make fertile* or productive 6

filter /'fɪltəʳ/ (1) an apparatus through which liquids are passed to remove solid material; (2) (verb) send through a filter RT 11

filtration /fɪl'treɪʃən/ RT 11

flour /flaʊəʳ/ powder made from grain, used for making bread, cakes etc. RT 7

fluid /'flu:ɪd/ substance* which flows – liquid or gas 1

formula /'fɔ:mjʊlə/ pl. **formulae** /'fɔ:mjuli:/ 4

friction /'frɪkʃən/ force which tries to stop one thing from slipping over another 1

fulcrum /'fʌlkrəm/ point on which a lever moves A

function /'fʌŋkʃən/ special purpose or use of something 5

galaxy /'gæləksɪ/ group of stars 4

gaseous /'geɪsɪəs, 'gæsɪəs/ 1

gauge /geɪdʒ/ 5

generalisation /,dʒenərəlaɪ'zeɪʃən/ statement about things in general 10

generally /'dʒenərəlɪ/ usually, mostly 1

geographical /,dʒɪə'græfɪkəl/ RT 2

germination /,dʒз:mɪ'neɪʃən/ 6

give off /,gɪv 'ɒf/ emit, send off 8

gland /glænd/ organ of the body which produces liquid substances* to be poured into the blood, or out of the body RT 5

glycogen /'glaɪkədʒən/ 5

green wood /'gri:n ,wʊd/ live wood 1

Greenwich /'grɪnɪdʒ/ a place near London, famous in astronomy RT 2

gritty /'grɪtɪ/ having small pieces of stone in it RT 1

hafnium /'hæfnɪəm/ (Hf) 2

heal /hi:l/ become healthy, grow new skin RT 7

height /haɪt/ 4

helium /'hi:lɪəm/ (He) 7

hemisphere /'hemɪsfɪəʳ/ 1

hollow /'hɒləʊ/ having an empty space inside 2

horizon /hə'raɪzən/ 6

horizontal /,hɒrɪ'zɒntl/ 1

hormone /'hɔ:məʊn/ RT 5

hydraulic /haɪ'drɔ:lɪk/ moved by the pressure of a liquid RT 9

hydrochloric /,haɪdrə'klɒrɪk/ 3

hydrogen /'haɪdrədʒən/ (H) 3

identify /aɪ'dentɪfaɪ/ say what something is, give it a name 8

ie /,aɪ'i:/ = that is 4

ignite /ɪg'naɪt/ 8

imaginary /ɪ'mædʒənərɪ/ not real, only in the mind RT 2

immediately /ɪ'mi:dɪətlɪ/ at once without a pause 6

inanimate /ɪn'ænɪmət/ without life 5

inert /ɪ'nз:t/ (of gases) forming no chemical compounds* C

injury /'ɪndʒərɪ/ wounds, such as cuts, broken bones etc. RT 7

instal /ɪn'stɔ:l/ fix in position for use 6

instrument /'ɪnstrəmənt/ apparatus used for precise work 5

interior /ɪn'tɪərɪəʳ/ 2

intermittently /ɪntə'mɪtəntlɪ/ at intervals 12

in terms of /ɪn 'tз:mz əv/ expressed as RT 11

internal /ɪn'tз:nəl/ of the inside 5

inverse /'ɪnvз:s/ 9

involve /ɪn'vɒlv/ require and include the action RT 11

iodine /'aɪədi:n/ (I) 8

iridium /aɪ'rɪdɪəm/ (Ir) 2

iron /'aɪən/ (Fe) RT 1

irrigate /'ɪrɪgeɪt/ supply water to land by

means of canals etc. 7

January /'dʒænjʊərɪ/ 4
July /dʒuːˈlaɪ/ 4
June /dʒuːn/ 4

Kilimanjaro /ˌkɪlɪmənˈdʒɑːrəʊ/ 4
kilo- /'kɪlə/ thousand 4
kilometre /kɪˈlɒmɪtəʳ, 'kɪləˌmiːtəʳ/ 4
krypton /'krɪptɒn/ (Kr) 7

label /'leɪbl/ put a name on something 11
laboratory /ləˈbɒrətrɪ/ 10
lanthanum /'lænθənəm/ (La) 2
latitude /'lætɪtjuːd/ RT 2
lay eggs /ˌleɪ 'egz/ produce eggs 10
layer /'leɪəʳ/ a thickness of some material
    laid over a surface RT 3
lay foundations /ˌleɪ faʊnˈdeɪʃənz/ build
    the supporting base of a building 6
lead /led/ (Pb) 7
length /leŋθ/ 4
level /'levəl/ make flat 6
liberate /'lɪbəreɪt/ release a gas from
    combination 8
likelihood /'laɪklɪhʊd/ probability* 10
limestone /'laɪmstəʊn/ RT 6
liquefaction /lɪkwɪˈfækʃən/ making liquid
    6
liquid /'lɪkwɪd/ 1
lithium /'lɪθɪəm/ (Li) 7
litmus paper /'lɪtməsˌpeɪpəʳ/ chemical
    indicator which turns red with an acid,
    blue with an alkali 8
litre /'liːtəʳ/ 4
liver /'lɪvəʳ/ 4
location /ləʊˈkeɪʃən/ 2
longitude /'lɒndʒɪtjuːd/ RT 2
longitudinal /ˌlɒndʒɪ'tjuːdɪnəl/ 1

magnesium /mægˈniːzɪəm/ (Mg) 7
magnetic /mægˈnetɪk/ able to pull objects
    made of certain metals (especially
    iron) towards it RT 1
maintain /meɪnˈteɪn/ keep something the
    same as it was before B
majority /məˈdʒɒrətɪ/ greater number or
    amount 9
mammal /'mæməl/ 10
manganese /'mæŋgəniːz/ (Mn) 2
manufacture /ˌmænjʊˈfæktʃəʳ/
    production 10
March /mɑːtʃ/ 4
mass /mæs/ quantity of material in a
    body 4
material /məˈtɪərɪəl/ 1
maximum /'mæksɪməm/ greatest size,

number etc. 4
May /meɪ/ 4
measurement /'meʒəmənt/ 4
membrane /'membreɪn/ soft thin layer
    which covers a cell or a part of the
    body RT 5
mercury /'mɜːkjərɪ/ (Hg) 2
meridian /məˈrɪdɪən/ line of longitude*
    RT 2
methane /'miːθeɪn/ (CH₄) 8
method /'meθəd/ way of doing
    something 11
metre /'miːtəʳ/ 4
metric /'metrɪk/ RT 4
micrometer /maɪˈkrɒmɪtəʳ/ 4
microscope /'maɪkrəskəʊp/ 5
migrate /maɪˈgreɪt/ move from one place
    to another 10
milli- /'mɪlɪ/ thousandth 4
minimum /'mɪnɪməm/ smallest size,
    number etc. 4
minority /maɪˈnɒrətɪ/ smaller number or
    amount 9
minute /'mɪnɪt/ (in the measurement of
    angles) the sixtieth part of a degree*,
    abbreviated as ' (eg 23° 27' N) RT 2
minute /maɪˈnjuːt/ very small 4
molecule /'mɒlɪkjuːl/ 4
molten /'məʊltn/ in the liquid state
    because of very high temperatures
    RT 3
molybdenum /məˈlɪbdənəm/ (Mo) 2
muscle /'mʌsəl/ organ in the body which
    produces movement RT 6

narrow /'nærəʊ/ (of range) small 4
negligible /'neglɪdʒəbəl/ 7
neon /'niːɒn/ (Ne) 1
neutralise /'njuːtrəlaɪz/ make neutral
    (neither acid nor alkaline) 8
nickel /'nɪkəl/ (Ni) RT 3
niobium /naɪˈəʊbɪəm/ (Nb) 2
nitre /'naɪtəʳ/ saltpetre (potassium nitrate
    KNO₃) 11
nitrogen /'naɪtrədʒən/ (N) RT 1
November /nəʊˈvembəʳ/ 4

obtain /əbˈteɪn/ get 8
occur /əˈkɜːʳ/ happen, be found 6
ocean /'əʊʃən/ 2
October /ɒkˈtəʊbəʳ/ 4
ohm /əʊm/ 4
opaque /əʊˈpeɪk/ 1
operate /'ɒpəreɪt/ make something work
    RT 8
organ /'ɔːgən/ part of a living body with a
    special function 5

organic /ɔːˈgænɪk/ found in living things 3

osmium /ˈɒzmɪəm/ (Os) 2

oxide /ˈɒksaɪd/ 8

oxygen /ˈɒksɪdʒən/ (O) 1

oxygenate /ˈɒksɪdʒəneɪt/ 5

palladium /pəˈleɪdɪəm/ (Pd) 2

pan /pæn/ part of a balance on which things are placed for weighing A

parallel /ˈpærəlel/ 1

particle /ˈpɑːtɪkəl/ very small piece of matter RT 5

pellagra /pəˈlægrə/ RT 7

per (normally unstressed) /pəʳ/ 4

percentage /pəˈsentɪdʒ/ number or rate in each hundred 7

phosphorous /ˈfɒsfərəs/ (P) 7

photosynthesis /ˌfəʊtəʊˈsɪnθəsɪs/ building up of sugars and starches in the green cells of a plant, by means of chlorophyll, in the presence of sunlight RT 6

pi /paɪ/ π ratio of circumference of a circle to its diameter (about 3·14159) 4

pipette /pɪˈpet/ 7

platinum /ˈplætɪnəm/ (Pt) 2

point of condensation /ˌpɔɪnt əv kɒndenˈseɪʃən/ point at which vapour becomes liquid 1

boiling point /ˈbɔɪlɪŋ ˌpɔɪnt/ point at which liquid becomes vapour 1

freezing point /ˈfriːzɪŋ ˌpɔɪnt/ point at which a liquid becomes solid 1

melting point /ˈmeltɪŋ ˌpɔɪnt/ point at which a solid becomes liquid 1

poisonous /ˈpɔɪzənəs/ dangerous if taken in by a living animal or plant RT 1

poles /pəʊlz/ the top and bottom points on the surface of the earth RT 2

pollen /ˈpɒlən) flower-dust carrying male cells 6

pollination /ˌpɒlɪˈneɪʃən/ carrying of pollen* to the female part of a flower 6

pollution /pəˈluːʃən/ the production of substances* which are harmful to the environment* RT 10

population /ˌpɒpjəˈleɪʃən/ number of people 7

over/under-populated /ˈəʊvə/ˈʌndə ˌpɒpjəleɪtɪd/ having too many/too few people 7

possess /pəˈzes/ have 7

potassium /pəˈtæsɪəm/ (K) 7

potential difference /pəˌtenʃəl ˈdɪfrəns/ difference of electric pressure 4

precede /prɪˈsiːd/ be before or in front of 6

precipitation /prɪˌsɪpɪˈteɪʃən/ fall of rain, snow etc. 6

prediction /prɪˈdɪkʃən/ saying in advance what will happen 10

pressure /ˈpreʃəʳ/ B

principle /ˈprɪnsɪpəl/ scientific rule or law RT 8

prior to /ˈpraɪə tʊ/ before 6

prism /ˈprɪzəm/ 1

proactinium /prəʊˈæktɪnɪəm/ (Pa) 8

probability /ˈprɒbəˈbɪlətɪ/ chance 10

procedure /prəˈsiːdʒəʳ/ way of doing something 11

process /ˈprəʊses/ 5

property /ˈprɒpətɪ/ special quality belonging to something 1

proportion /prəˈpɔːʃən/ size of something when thought of as part of a whole, or in relation to something else 9

prove /pruːv/ show that something is true 12

provided that /prəˈvaɪdɪd ðət/ (only) if 10

quantity /ˈkwɒntətɪ/ 7

radiate /ˈreɪdɪeɪt/ send out energy 5

radiation /ˌreɪdɪˈeɪʃən/ energy sent out (eg heat or light) RT 10

radiator /ˈreɪdɪeɪtəʳ/ 5

radioactive /ˌreɪdɪəʊˈæktɪv/ 8

radium /ˈreɪdɪəm/ (Ra) 7

radius /ˈreɪdɪəs/ 4

range /reɪndʒ/ distance or change between fixed point 4

rapid /ˈræpɪd/ quick, fast RT 9

ratio /ˈreɪʃɪəʊ/ 9

react /rɪˈækt/ change chemically when mixed with another substance* RT 1

rectangular /rekˈtæŋgjələʳ/ 6

refinery /rɪˈfaɪnərɪ/ building or apparatus in which pure forms of oil are produced from crude oil RT 11

refrigerator /rɪˈfrɪdʒəreɪtəʳ/ 6

region /ˈriːdʒən/ large area 12

relatively /ˈrelətɪvlɪ/ when compared* with others 9

remote /rɪˈməʊt/ (of chance) very small 10

repel /rɪˈpel/ push away (by magnetism) 8

reptile /ˈreptaɪl/ 10

residue /ˈrezɪdjuː/ that which remains 11

resistance /rɪˈzɪstəns/ the ability of a substance* to remain unchanged when acted on by a force 4

respiration /ˌrespɪˈreɪʃən/ the action of breathing; the intake of oxygen by a living organism RT 6

respiratory /rɪˈspɪrətərɪ, ˈrespɪreɪtərɪ/ RT 5

result /rɪˈzʌlt/ that which a cause produces 8

rhenium /ˈriːnɪəm/ (Re) 2

rhodium /ˈrəʊdɪəm/ (Rh) 2

rickets /ˈrɪkɪts/ RT 7

right angle /ˈraɪt ˌæŋɡəl/ an angle of 90° 1

rigid /ˈrɪdʒɪd/ 1

roughly /ˈrʌflɪ/ 1

row /rəʊ/ 2

ruthenium /ruːˈθiːnɪəm/ (Ru) 2

saturated solution /ˌsætʃʊreɪtɪd səˈluːʃən/ a solution which contains so much of the dissolved substance* that no more can be dissolved at that temperature 11

scale /skeɪl/ (1) series of marks at regular intervals for the purpose of measuring A; (2) size of a map etc. in relation to what it represents 9

scandium /ˈskændɪəm/ (Sc) 2

scurvy /ˈskɜːvɪ/ RT 7

seal /siːl/ close tightly B

secrete /sɪˈkriːt/ produce a liquid substance* which is useful to the body RT 5

seismology /saɪzˈmɒlədʒɪ/ 12

September /sepˈtembər/ 4

sequence /ˈsiːkwəns/ order of events 6

sieve /sɪv/ press through wire net in order to separate different substances* 11

silicon /ˈsɪlɪkɒn/ (Si) 7

silvery /ˈsɪlvərɪ/ having the colour of silver (Ag) RT 1

simultaneous /ˌsɪməlˈteɪnɪəs/ happening at the same time 6

site /saɪt/ piece of ground where a building is or will be built 6

sodium /ˈsəʊdɪəm/ (Na) RT 1

solder /ˈsəʊldər/ alloy used to join metals together 9

solidification /səˌlɪdɪfɪˈkeɪʃən/ the change from the liquid or gaseous state into the solid state RT 3

soluble /ˈsɒljʊbəl/ 1

spatial /ˈspeɪʃəl/ in relation to space 4

speedometer /spiːˈdɒmɪtər/ 5

sphere /sfɪər/ 1

spherical /ˈsferɪkəl/ 1

spiral /ˈspaɪərəl/ A

standard /ˈstændəd/ measurement with which other measurements or measuring instruments* can be compared RT 4

standardise /ˈstændədaɪz/ cause to conform to a standard* RT 4

state /steɪt/ condition 1

stir /stɜːr/ mix with a cylindrical rod 11

store /stɔːr/ keep in one place for later use 5

strip /strɪp/ thin piece of material RT 8

stroke /strəʊk/ rub gently 11

strontium /ˈstrɒntɪəm/ (Sr) 7

structure /ˈstrʌktʃər/ 3

sublimation /ˌsʌbləˈmeɪʃən/ RT 11

sublime /səˈblaɪm/ change a solid into a vapour 8

substance /ˈsʌbstəns/ (particular kind of) matter 3

suckle /ˈsʌkəl/ feed with milk from the breast or udder 10

sufficient /səˈfɪʃənt/ enough 7

suitable /ˈsuːtəbəl, ˈsjuːtəbəl/ right or proper for a particular purpose 1

sulphide /ˈsʌlfaɪd/ RT 3

sulphur /ˈsʌlfər/ (S) 7

supply /səˈplaɪ/ give or provide 5

support /səˈpɔːt/ provide enough for 7

surface /ˈsɜːfɪs/ 1

surface tension /ˌsɜːfɪs ˈtenʃən/ 8

swell /swel/ grow larger 6

synthesis /ˈsɪnθəsɪs/ RT 11

synthetic /sɪnˈθetɪk/ made by man, not natural 10

system /ˈsɪstəm/ a group of parts working together RT 5

tantalum /ˈtæntələm/ (Ta) 2

tapering /ˈteɪpərɪŋ/ 1

technetium /tekˈniːʃɪəm/ (Tc) 2

technology /tekˈnɒlədʒɪ/ the use of science in industry, industrial methods RT 10

temperate /ˈtempərət/ (of climate) not too hot or cold 7

temperature /ˈtempərətʃər/ RT 1

test /test/ find the quality, composition etc. by examination 11

thermometer /θəˈmɒmɪtər/ 5

thermostat /ˈθɜːməstæt/ instrument* which keeps temperature at one level RT 8

thorium /ˈθɔːrɪəm/ (Th) 8

thyroid /ˈθaɪrɔɪd/ gland in the neck which controls the development of mind and body RT 5

tissue /ˈtɪʃuː, ˈtɪsjuː/ material made of cells of the same type, making up particular organs of the body, or parts of organs RT 5

titanium /taɪˈteɪnɪəm/ (Ti) 2

total /ˈtəʊtl/ added together 4

tough /tʌf/ 1

translucent /trænzˈluːsənt/ 1

transmit /trænzˈmɪt/ send from one place to another RT 9

transparent /trænˈspærənt/ 1

transport /ˈtrænspɔːt/ the carrying of people and goods from one place to another RT 10

triangular /traɪˈæŋgjələr/ 1

tripod /ˈtraɪpɒd/ 1

tropical /ˈtrɒpɪkəl/ between the Tropic of Cancer* and the Tropic of Capricorn* RT 2

Tropic of Cancer /ˌtrɒpɪk əv ˈkænsər/ RT 2

Tropic of Capricorn /ˌtrɒpɪk əv ˈkæprɪkɔːn/ RT 2

trough /trɒf/ 1

tungsten /ˈtʌŋstən/ (W) 2

unit /ˈjuːnɪt/ quantity or amount used as a standard measurement 4

uranium /jʊˈreɪnɪəm/ (U) 7

urinary /ˈjʊərɪnərɪ/ RT 5

valve /vælv/ 8

vanadium /vəˈneɪdɪəm/ (V) 2

vaporised /ˈveɪpəraɪzd/ converted* into vapour 5

vapour /ˈveɪpər/ RT 11

vary /ˈveərɪ/ be different, change 4

vena cava /ˌviːnə ˈkeɪvə/ B

ventricle /ˈventrɪkəl/ 8

vertical /ˈvɜːtɪkəl/ 1

violently /ˈvaɪələntlɪ/ strongly and quickly RT 1

vital /ˈvaɪtl/ necessary for life RT 7

vitamin /ˈvɪtəmɪn, ˈvaɪtəmɪn/ RT 7

volcano /vɒlˈkeɪnəʊ/ 6

volt /vəʊlt/ 4

volume /ˈvɒljuːm/ 4

waste matter /ˌweɪst ˈmætər/ substances* which are not needed by the body, and which are ejected* by it RT 5

watt /wɒt/ 4

wavelength /ˈweɪvleŋθ/ the distance between one (electromagnetic) wave and another RT 4

wax /wæks/ soft yellow substance produced by bees, also obtained from petroleum 12

weight /weɪt/ 4

well-balanced /ˌwel ˈbælənst/ containing the right amounts and proportions of substances* which are good for the body RT 7

wholemeal /ˈhəʊlmiːl/ made from the complete grain (without removing the covering of the grain) RT 7

width /wɪtθ/ 4

xenon /ˈzenɒn/ (Xe) 7

yttrium /ˈɪtrɪəm/ (Y) 2

zero /ˈzɪərəʊ/ the number 0 RT 2

zirconium /zɜːˈkəʊnɪəm/ (Zr) 2